£6.45NJ

COLLINS CLASSICS PLUS

Th 241 e Woman in White

INTE'

D'R

TR

WA

T

Adapted by
Keith West

Series Consultant
Cecily O'Neill

D1611058

Author's dedication To the Piker family. People say that friends are friends but relations are nuisances. You are all exceptions. I am pleased that all five you are my friends AND relations – and people who appreciate literature. My gratitude to my family and friends, who have helped and encouraged me.

Published by Collins Educational, an imprint of HarperCollins*Publishers* Ltd 77–85 Fulham Palace Road, London W6 8JB

First published 1999 . Reprinted 1999

ISBN 000 323 077 5

British Library Cataloguing in Publication Data
A catalogue record for this book is available from the British Library.

Commissioned by Helen Clark, edited by Katie Taylor and Toby Satterthwaite, picture research by Catherine Dey

Design by Nigel Jordan, cover design by Nigel Jordan, cover illustration by Alan Marks

Acknowledgements
The following permissions to reproduce material are gratefully acknowledged:
Illustrations: Nigel Jordan, p. 45; Mary Evans Picture Library, p. 49, 67, 69; by courtesy of the National Portrait Gallery, London, p. 58; Wellcome Institute Library, London, p.65.
Text extracts: BBC, p. 54; thanks to *The Female Malady* by Elaine Showalter (Virago) for help with pp. 64–66; extract from *The Independent*, p. 70; The Woman in Black by Susan Hill, courtesy of Addison, Wesley, Longman, pp. 73–74; 'Waly, Waly', from *I'll Tell you a Tale* by Ian Serraillier, courtesy of Puffin Books, pp. 74–75.
Whilst every effort has been made both to contact the copyright holders and to give exact credit lines, this has not proved possible in every case.

Production by Susan Cashin, printed and bound in Hong Kong

For permission to perform this play, please allow plenty of time and contact:
Permissions Department, HarperCollins*Publishers*,
77–85 Fulham Palace Road, London W6 8JB. Tel. 0181 741 7070.

Contents

	KEY
71-74 / **71-74**	cross-reference between playscript and teaching resources.
H	in resources = activity suitable for homework.

Characters

THE FAIRLIE FAMILY AND FRIENDS

Laura Fairlie heir to the Limmeridge estate.
Marian Halcombe half-sister of Laura Fairlie.
Frederick Fairlie uncle of Laura. Grey haired, pale and sickly.
Mr Gilmore the Fairlies' family lawyer.

THE CATHERICKS

Anne Catherick the woman in white.
Mrs Catherick Anne's mother.

SIR PERCIVAL GLYDE AND FRIENDS

Sir Percival Glyde baronet, engaged to Laura Fairlie. Tall and thin.
Mr Merriman Sir Percival's lawyer.
Count Fosco a fat Italian friend of Sir Percival.
Fosco's Maid
Sir Percival's Maid

WALTER HARTRIGHT AND FRIENDS

Walter Hartright a young painter.
Professor Pesca an old Italian friend of Walter.

OTHER CHARACTERS

Guard
Clerk
Man
Policeman
Beggar
Nurses
Street Vendors

The Woman In White

ACT ONE

The stage has no permanent set. The chairs used in the opening scenes are arranged on the stage. They remain on the stage throughout the play. See *Staging the Play*, page 45.

45 ▶

Scene One

Limmeridge graveyard. It is dark. A white gravestone with an angel on it gleams in the moonlight. A ghostly figure of a woman dressed in white appears. She has a white face, as if she is made of marble. She stares at the audience, then gives a blood-curdling scream. There is laughter, as if from a mad woman, offstage, then a blackout.

45 ▶

Scene Two

A road at night. **Walter** *enters, deep in conversation with* **Professor Pesca.** *Pesca appears to notice the audience, nudges* **Walter** *and points at them.*

55 ▶

WALTER *(to audience)* Ladies and gentlemen, forgive me. Allow me to introduce myself. My name is Walter Hartright. *(he bows)* This gentleman is my old friend, Professor Pesca. *(Pesca bows dramatically to the audience)* We were just now deep in conversation recalling certain extraordinary events which took place some years ago. I was then a young, impoverished painter. With the help of my old Italian friend, *(he indicates Pesca, who again bows)* I had just secured a position at Limmeridge House, Cumberland.

PESCA *(excitedly and with a strong Italian accent)* My good dear, what did I say after you saved me from drowning? I said that I should never be happy again till I had found the opportunity of doing a good something for my dear friend Walter. In finding you the job at Limmeridge House, the something was done at last. The only word to say is right-all-right! But I promise, course-of-course, to help you further if I can. *(**Pesca** exits, chattering excitedly to himself in Italian)*

WALTER *(shakes his head in amusement at Pesca's high spirits)* I was to teach Mr Fairlie's nieces the art of painting in water colours. The evening before leaving London, I had visited my mother to say good-bye and was returning to my chambers. *(he starts walking, as if along a road)* I was thinking about my prospects, when I saw in front of me the figure of a woman. *(Pause. Lights come up to show the **woman in white** standing beside the road to London)* She was dressed from head to foot in white. *(whispering)* At first I thought she was a ghost – until she spoke.

WOMAN IN WHITE *(pointing offstage)* Is that the road to London? *(pause)* Did you hear me? I asked if that was the way to London.

WALTER Yes, that is the way. It leads to St John's Wood and the Regent's Park. You must excuse me, I was rather startled by your sudden appearance and…

WOMAN IN WHITE *(quickly)* You don't suspect me of doing anything wrong, do you? I have done nothing wrong. I have met here with an accident. Why do you suspect me of doing wrong?

WALTER *(taken aback)* I suspect you of nothing. I only wish to be of assistance to you.

WOMAN IN WHITE *(grasping **Walter**'s arm)* May I trust you? Do you know many people in London? Many men of rank and title?

WALTER *(hesitating)* Some. Why do you ask?

WOMAN IN WHITE Because I hope, for my own sake, there is one baronet that you don't know.

WALTER Will you tell me his name?

WOMAN IN WHITE *(very agitated)* I can't – I daren't – I forgot myself when I mentioned it.

WALTER I am afraid the baronet has done you some wrong. Is he the cause of you being out here alone at this strange time of night?

WOMAN IN WHITE *(nearly crying)* Don't ask me. Don't make me talk of it. I have been cruelly wronged. I ask again, do you know many men of rank and title?

WALTER Not many. I am only a poor artist – a drawing master.

WOMAN IN WHITE Not a man of rank and title yourself? Thank God! I may trust you! *(pause)* Do you live in London?

WALTER Yes... but tomorrow I'm moving north to Cumberland.

WOMAN IN WHITE *(shocked)* Cumberland! I was once happy in Cumberland. Limmeridge House... I should like to see that place again. My friend Mrs Fairlie is now dead, but if there are any still there of that name I love them for her sake.

WALTER *(very surprised)* What? But that's where I...

The sound of running footsteps and indistinct voices interrupts him.

WOMAN IN WHITE *(quickly)* Did you hear voices? Was anybody calling after us? I think I heard something! *(very distressed)* I must go. Thank you, thank you. *(she kisses **Walter**'s hand and runs offstage)*

WALTER *(undecided, wanting to follow her)* Wait!

*A **policeman** strolls onstage and another **man** runs up to him. **Walter** pulls back into the shadows and watches them.*

MAN *(breathless)* Officer... Have you seen a woman pass this way? A woman dressed in white?

POLICEMAN *(hesitating)* I haven't seen her, sir.

MAN *(giving the **policeman** a card)* If you see her, stop her, and take her to this address. I'll pay all expenses, and a fair reward into the bargain.

POLICEMAN Why are we to stop her, sir? What has she done?

MAN Done? She has escaped from my asylum. Don't forget – a woman in white. She's quite mad, sir!

*He runs off, followed by the **policeman** at a stroll. **Walter** is alone on stage. He emerges from the shadows, looking stunned.*

Scene Three

45 *The breakfast room in Limmeridge House. **Marian** is looking out of the window with her back to the audience. **Walter** stands to one side downstage, with a suitcase.*

WALTER *(to audience)* Next day, during my train journey to Carlisle, I thought of nothing else but the woman in white and the coincidence concerning Limmeridge House. What had I done? I had seen nothing in her language or her actions that suggested she was mad. I arrived at Limmeridge House too late at night to meet anyone, except a servant. *(a servant comes on and takes Walter's suitcase. He yawns)* The following morning, I rose early and sauntered downstairs. *(walks across the stage)* There I met a... *(he hesitates)* ...masculine-looking young lady, who turned out to be one of the sisters I was to tutor in art.

*Walter crosses into the breakfast room. **Marian** turns as **Walter** enters.*

MARIAN *(enthusiastically)* Mr Hartright? Allow me to introduce myself. I'm Marian Halcombe, one of your pupils. Shall we shake hands? We must sooner or later – and why not sooner?

They shake hands.

WALTER Miss Halcombe...?

MARIAN I see your confusion, Mr Hartright – I am half-sister to your other pupil, Laura Fairlie. Our mother was married twice. Perhaps I should explain that, except for the fact that we are both orphans, Laura and I are completely unlike. My father was poor, Miss Fairlie's father was rich. I have nothing, she has a fortune. *(she laughs, with no bitterness)* I am dark and ugly, she is fair and pretty. In short she is an angel and I am... not. I won't live without her and she can't live without me. I shall be your only company at breakfast this morning. My sister is in her room nursing a slight headache. She is not strong.

WALTER And Mr Fairlie?

MARIAN Laura's uncle and guardian, Mr Fairlie, never joins us at
our meals. He's an invalid – I don't know what is the matter with
him, and the doctor doesn't know, and he himself doesn't know!
I shall take you to see him. He will want to see you as soon as
possible. Do I talk too much?

WALTER *(laughs)* Not at all, Miss Fair... Halcombe.

MARIAN Good. Will you enjoy yourself here, Mr Hartright?
Everything is quiet and humdrum here. Won't you thirst for
adventure?

WALTER I have had enough adventures recently. The very evening
before I arrived at this house, I had an adventure.

MARIAN May I hear it?

WALTER You have a claim to. On my way in to London, I chanced
upon a strange young woman, dressed in white. She may be a
total stranger to you, as she was to me, but she mentioned the
name of your late mother with gratitude and affection. I have to
tell you that a man from an asylum came looking for her, but I
have no reason to believe she was mad. Have you an idea who
she may be?

MARIAN None! I am all aflame with curiosity. However, my sister
and I have a large collection of my mother's letters. While you see
Mr Fairlie, I will pass the morning looking through them to see if
I can discover anything. Please say nothing of this to my sister or
Mr Fairlie, who are both, in different ways, nervous and sensitive.
Come, I shall take you to Mr Fairlie on the instant. Follow me!

Scene Four

*Mr Fairlie's room at Limmeridge House. It is very dim. **Mr Fairlie** is
sitting in a chair, with a blanket on his knees. He is inspecting coins placed
near him on a small table containing bottles of medicine. He places a small
brush on the table. **Walter** enters.*

45

MR FAIRLIE *(in a faint, quavering voice)* So glad you came to
Limmeridge, Mr Hartright. *(he takes a handkerchief from his pocket*

and holds it to his nose) Pray, sit down. *(he winces as **Walter** starts to move a chair)* Don't trouble yourself to move the chair, please. In the wretched state of my nerves, movement of any kind is most painful to me. Have you seen your room? Will it do?

WALTER I have just come from the...

MR FAIRLIE *(cuts **Walter** off, closes his eyes, covers them with one hand and holds the other up in alarm)* Pray, excuse me. But please do speak in a lower key. In the wretched state of my nerves, loud sounds are a torture to me. Will you pardon an invalid? And you like your room?

WALTER *(quietly)* I could not wish for anything better.

MR FAIRLIE Good, good. Do you mind handing me those coins on the table? My nerves are such that any movement will affect me. Do you like coins?

WALTER Yes, I have...

MR FAIRLIE Good. Can you undertake to teach Miss Fairlie and Miss Halcombe how to draw? Do you mind my closing my eyes while I speak? This morning light is too bright for them.

WALTER Mr Fairlie, I...

MR FAIRLIE Ah, yes! The ladies who profit from your services, Mr Hartright, must decide for themselves about the instruction you give them. They know what they want, I am sure. I will not keep you. Such a relief to have done business with you. Would you carry the coins out for me? How nice to be so strong. Take great care not to bang the doors as you leave. The slightest noise goes through me like a knife.

__Walter__ leaves __Mr Fairlie__, who shakes his head and takes a deep breath.

Scene Five

*Lights fade and then brighten, to indicate a passage of time. **Walter** and **Marian** are walking in the grounds of Limmeridge House.*

MARIAN Mr Hartright, how did you get on with Mr Fairlie? Was he particularly plagued with his nerves this morning?

WALTER *(not knowing how to answer)* Well… actually…

MARIAN *(laughs)* Let me guess: you started to speak with him and he asked you to talk in a lower key because of the poor state of his nerves? Is that not so?

Before he can answer, a delicate blue-eyed young woman, clothed in a simple white muslin dress and carrying a basket, enters. She stoops to pick a flower and place it in the basket.

MARIAN Ah, let me introduce you to my sister, Miss Laura Fairlie. Your model pupil found at last, Mr Hartright.

WALTER *(bowing courteously)* Miss Fairlie.

LAURA *(shyly)* Mr Hartright. I am so glad you have come. Though I am so conscious of my own ignorance in drawing that I am more afraid than anxious to begin. *(she wanders off around the garden, picking flowers)*

MARIAN *(drawing **Walter** to one side)* Mr Hartright, I have some news concerning the lady you met on the road to London. *(she takes a letter from her pocket)* I have found a letter written by my mother, eleven years ago. A Mrs Catherick from Hampshire came here to nurse her sick sister and my mother looked after Mrs Catherick's child, Anne. The girl was rather slow at learning, but was grateful. My mother gave her some white frocks Laura had grown out of. She said to my mother *(she reads from the letter)* "I will always wear white as long as I live. It will help me to remember you, ma'am." Now, the woman you saw on the road to London, you say she was dressed all in white?

WALTER All in white.

*He looks across at **Laura**, as if a thought had just occurred to him.*

MARIAN You see it too, just as my dear mother did eleven years ago. Anne Catherick resembles my half-sister, Laura.

WALTER The very living likeness, in her hair, her complexion, the colour of her eyes, the shape of her face.

MARIAN Exactly as my mother wrote.

WALTER (*continues to gaze at* **Laura**. *He is stunned by her beauty.* **Marian** *goes to join her sister.* **Walter** *speaks to the audience*) She was the first woman to ever quicken my pulse. No one else had ever stirred me in this way before. I was halfway in love with her in that first moment. And yet, there was something that troubled me; something not quite right. I saw Miss Fairlie's likeness to Anne Catherick unwillingly. To link that friendless, lost woman with Miss Fairlie seemed to cast a shadow on her bright future. I had a deep foreboding, as if fate was against us before we even knew each other. But how delightful the next three months were to be...

Music. **Walter** *crosses to where* **Laura** *is drawing. He looks over her shoulder and touches her hand as he guides her drawing. She looks up at him and they smile. All this is observed by* **Marian**, *who is frowning.* **Laura** *walks offstage with her drawing,* **Walter** *waves to her and she blows him a kiss.* **Laura** *walks back onstage with new drawings.* **Walter** *studies them with his arm over her shoulder,* **Marian** *shakes her head. The lights come up.*

MARIAN (*to audience*) If I had known three months earlier what would follow, would I have introduced my sister to Walter Hartright with such a light heart? I could see that he loved her. There was no doubt of his worth, but there was so much he did not know. It was my duty to enlighten him. (*she turns to* **Walter**, *who is now holding hands with* **Laura**. **Marian** *approaches, looking stern.* **Walter** *is embarrassed*) Mr Hartright, can I speak with you a moment?

Walter *leaves* **Laura** *sketching and goes to* **Marian**.

MARIAN (*looks at* **Walter** *thoughtfully*) Mr Hartright, I am going to tell you, at once, in my own plain, blunt, downright language, that I have discovered your secret.

WALTER Secret?

MARIAN You have thoughtlessly allowed yourself to form an attachment to my sister, Laura. I blame the misfortune on your years and position. (**Walter** *looks ashamed and does not meet* **Marian**'s *eyes*) I do not blame you. I have given you pain and must give you more, there is no help for it. Shake hands with your friend, Marian Halcombe.

They shake hands. She looks at him and shakes her head sadly.

MARIAN The hard and cruel question that we must face is that there are social inequalities. There is a difference in rank and station. You must leave Limmeridge House immediately, before more harm is done. You must leave us, not because you are a teacher of drawing only, but because Laura Fairlie is engaged to be married.

WALTER *(sinks to his knees in despair)* I love her as no man has ever loved a woman.

MARIAN Crush your feelings for her. Tear out your feelings, trample them under foot, act like a man!

WALTER *(rises to his feet. He struggles to speak)* I will do what is best for Laura. I ask your pardon and hers.

MARIAN My sister has suffered the secret misery of self-reproach since the first shadow of a feeling disloyal to her engagement entered her heart. The man she is to marry has never had a strong hold on her affections. It is an engagement of honour, not love; her father sanctioned it on his deathbed.

WALTER I will leave tomorrow. We have understood each other. May I ask the name of the gentleman to whom Miss Fairlie is engaged?

MARIAN She is engaged to a baronet: Sir Percival Glyde.

Marian exits.

WALTER *(to audience)* A baronet? Why did this bring back my meeting with Anne Catherick? However sharp my suffering at leaving Laura, I had a still stronger sense of an invisible threat waiting for us all. How much more difficult to leave Laura to face this threat without me! Yet it was for her good that I had to prepare to leave immediately.

Scene Six

Walter's room at Limmeridge House. He is packing his belongings, including clothes and painting equipment, into several suitcases. There is an urgent knocking at the door. Walter looks up as Marian comes in clutching a letter.

MARIAN *(angry and agitated)* I had hoped that painful subjects of conversation were at an end for today. But there is a plot to frighten my sister about her approaching marriage. She has received a letter – an anonymous letter. *(she waves the letter at Walter)* It mentions her forthcoming marriage to Sir Percival Glyde and describes him intimately – the red scar on the back of his hand, his dry hacking cough, his brown eyes and his small delicate hands. The writer knows this man well.

WALTER How may I help with this matter, Miss Halcombe?

MARIAN You are the only person in the house or out of it who can advise me. Allow me to read you part of the letter.

WALTER Certainly.

MARIAN *(reading from the letter)* "Miss Fairlie – I beg of you, believe in dreams. Last night I dreamt about you, Miss Fairlie, and I woke with my eyes full of tears and my heart beating. I dreamt you were married to this man and you were not happy, he was cruel to you. Inquire into the past life of that man before you say the words that make you his miserable wife. I have an interest in your wellbeing. Your mother was kind to me, she is dead and so you have a tender place in my heart: your mother was my first, my best, my only friend…" And the letter goes on to describe Sir Percival, exactly as he is physically, although he is portrayed as an evil man who loves only himself.

WALTER *(takes the letter from her and reads)* This is an astonishing letter. Tell me plainly, have you any reason not to trust Sir Percival Glyde?

MARIAN None whatsoever. I have full confidence in Sir Percival's reputation. It seems to me that whoever wrote this letter must have a mind that is…

WALTER Mad?

MARIAN Yes. There is more. Strange things have been seen at my mother's grave in the village by the local schoolchildren.

WALTER Let us not lose any time – we must go and investigate at once. All of these strange happenings must be linked in some way.

Scene Seven

Limmeridge graveyard. It is dark. The gravestone with the angel gleams in the moonlight. The **woman in white** *enters slowly, carrying a bunch of white flowers. She kneels at the grave. Her face is covered in a veil. She places the flowers before the grave, reaches out to touch it, and then kisses it. From her pocket she takes a white cloth and starts to clean the stone.* **Walter** *comes in. He pauses to watch her for a moment, then walks slowly up to her.*

WALTER *(quietly)* Hello, Anne Catherick.

Anne *jumps up, startled. She is ready to run, like a hunted animal.*

WALTER Don't be frightened. Surely you remember me?

ANNE *(hesitates)* You were kind to me once. What are you doing here?

WALTER Can you talk to me without feeling frightened? I have been staying, since we last met, at Limmeridge House.

ANNE *(looking more confident)* At Limmeridge House?

WALTER How did you come here?

ANNE Where should I go if not here? I came to clean the grave of the friend who was better than a mother to me.

WALTER I felt very uneasy about you after you left me; a strange thing happened. I overheard a man talking to a policeman. He said you had escaped from an asylum.

Anne *makes to run away.*

WALTER Stop and hear how I helped you. One word from me would have told the man which way you had gone – and I never spoke that word.

ANNE You don't think I ought to be back in the asylum, do you? You don't think I ought to be taken back, do you?

WALTER *(softly, walking towards her)* Certainly not. I am glad I helped you escape.

ANNE Mrs Fairlie would have helped me. Mrs Fairlie knew best. She was fond of white and there is white stone about her grave. She often wore white and dressed her daughter in white. Is Miss Fairlie well and happy?

WALTER Miss Fairlie is neither well nor happy, because she has received your letter. You mention no names in your letter, but Miss Fairlie knows that the person you write of is Sir Percival Glyde.

Anne screams.

ANNE Sir Percival – you know too much, you frighten me. I am all afraid. Beware Sir Percival – beware!

WALTER Why? And what are you doing here? Anne...

Anne runs offstage. Walter lets her go, not wanting to frighten her. The lights come up. Laura is walking towards the grave, carrying cut flowers.

LAURA Mr Hartright!

WALTER Miss Fairlie.

Laura places the flowers on her mother's grave.

LAURA Somebody has already put flowers here. *(she hesitates)* I am very sorry you are going away. Oh, how could I let you go after we have passed so many happy days together?

WALTER I shall remember those kind words, Miss Fairlie, long after tomorrow has come and gone.

LAURA *(tearfully)* Don't speak of tomorrow. Let us walk back to the house together.

They join arms and walk slowly along. They are met by Marian.

MARIAN I am sorry you are going, Mr Hartright. *(looking at Laura)* I know it is for the best.

LAURA *(starts to cry softly)* For God's sake, leave us Mr Hartright.

Laura hurries away.

MARIAN I have heard and seen more than you think. Your behaviour has made me your friend for life. Should you ever need me, should you ever want for anything…

WALTER *(bursts out)* She loves me, I know it!

MARIAN Better for you and for her that you leave us now. *(she takes his hand)* I will trust you as my friend, as her friend, as our brother. God bless you, Walter. If only Laura were not engaged, I am sure my uncle would not make your social position an obstacle… Go, Walter, go!

*Walter exits, dejected. The lights go down, leaving the spotlight on **Marian**.*

MARIAN *(to audience)* Had I done the right thing? I knew they loved each other, but it was her father's death-bed wish… And Walter was poor. I knew no harm of Sir Percival, and yet… The woman in white troubled me – the time had come to tell Laura about her. Who could I consult? Mr Fairlie wanted only what was least trouble to him, not what was best for Laura. To whom could I turn for advice that I could trust? *(**Mr Gilmore**, the Fairlies' family lawyer, enters)* Mr Gilmore! How do you do? What brings you to Limmeridge House so unexpectedly?

MR GILMORE *(clasping her hand)* How do you do, my dear? I have come to Limmeridge House to consult with Mr Fairlie, as I have heard from Sir Percival's lawyer regarding Miss Fairlie's marriage settlement.

MARIAN It may be that you can help me with another matter that closely concerns Sir Percival and an unfortunate young woman, Anne Catherick, who has some connection with Limmeridge House and Laura.

MR GILMORE If I may be of service in my legal capacity, my dear, you have only to ask.

MARIAN Then allow me to take you indoors and make you comfortable. Then perhaps I may venture to confide in you, as so often in the past.

Marian exits with Mr Gilmore.

Scene Eight

Mr Fairlie's room. Mr Fairlie is sitting in his chair. Mr Gilmore knocks loudly and Mr Fairlie winces and places a silk handkerchief over his face. Mr Gilmore enters. Mr Gilmore waits for Mr Fairlie to look at him. He goes right up to him to peer closely at him, then becomes impatient.

MR GILMORE *(loudly)* I have come here to serve the interests of your niece and your family and I think I have a claim to your attention in return.

MR FAIRLIE *(weakly removing the handkerchief)* Don't bully me! Please don't bully me! I'm not strong enough.

MR GILMORE My object is to ask you to protect your niece. Sir Percival Glyde insists that if Miss Fairlie were to die before him, her fortune would go to him. My conscience forces me to tell you that that money should return to her family in the event of her death. Stand firm against Sir Percival's demand!

MR FAIRLIE I would argue with you if I could, but I can't – I haven't stamina enough. You want to upset me, Glyde, yourself and Laura. And all for the sake of something that is unlikely to happen. You must remember that Sir Percival is considerably older than Laura. No, dear friend, in the interests of peace and quiet, no!

MR GILMORE *(sighs)* Whatever happens, sir, remember that my plain duty of warning you has been performed. Good day to you.

Mr Gilmore leaves. Mr Fairlie lies back and replaces the handkerchief on his face.

Scene Nine

The grounds at Limmeridge House. Marian and Mr Gilmore enter, arm in arm.

MR GILMORE I may have failed to persuade Mr Fairlie to act in Miss Fairlie's best interests, but I have been successful in serving you in one respect. Before I leave for London, I have some news for you on the subject of Anne Catherick.

MARIAN Have we confirmation of our suspicion that Sir Percival Glyde was involved with her confinement in an asylum?

MR GILMORE With Sir Percival's permission, I wrote to Anne's mother, Mrs Catherick, and have received by return of post a letter from her. *(he takes out a letter and reads)* "Sir, I am pleased to confirm that my daughter Anne was placed under medical care with my full knowledge and approval. The role played by Sir Percival Glyde in the matter was fully honourable. He deserves my gratitude. Your obedient servant, Anne Jane Catherick."

*He hands the letter to **Marian** to look at.*

MARIAN Sir Percival's character has been fully established.

MR GILMORE Beyond all doubt, my dear Miss Halcombe.

They say goodbye affectionately and exit.

Scene Ten

*Walter, **Marian** and **Laura** are in three pools of light.*

WALTER *(reads from a letter. He looks up and speaks to himself, as if to master his emotions)* I shall sail to Central America and start a new life for myself. I'll never forget Laura, never! *(he exits)*

MARIAN *(to Laura)* So you are to be married and away to a honeymoon in Italy for six months. I may never see you again, my dear sister. With all your wealth and all your beauty, how friendless you are. The one man who would give his life to serve you is sailing to Central America this very night. Who else is left to you? Only me... and Sir Percival. And I do not like that man, even though he will be your husband! *(she exits)*

*Organ music. A multi-coloured light is cast across the stage, like sunlight through stained glass. **Laura** takes out a veil, places it on her head, and walks slowly towards the front of the stage, as if along an aisle. As she does so, the organ music gets louder and louder. When she reaches the front, there is a sudden blackout and silence.*

ACT TWO
Scene One

The library at Blackwater Park, home of Sir Percival Glyde. **Sir Percival** *and* **Count Fosco** *are in conversation.* **Marian** *enters.*

SIR PERCIVAL *(turning to see her)* Miss Halcombe, welcome to my home, Blackwater Park. Allow me *(cough)* to introduce you to my dear friend, Count Fosco. Fosco, my sister-in-law.

COUNT FOSCO I am charmed to meet you, Miss Halcombe.

She nods and holds out her hand for him to shake, but he bows and kisses her hand, then holds on to it.

COUNT FOSCO I have heard so much about you from your dear sister, Lady Glyde. Sir Percival is indeed a fortunate man.

SIR PERCIVAL Yes, quite so.

The sound of vicious barking is heard outside.

COUNT FOSCO *(letting go of* **Marian**'s *hand)* Your groom warned me about your dog, Percival.

SIR PERCIVAL It flies at everyone.

COUNT FOSCO *(pompously walking around the room)* Because everyone is afraid of him. I put my plump fingers on the brute's head and called it a coward. Then I stared into its eyes. All big dogs are cowards, Sir Percival. Anything your dog can surprise unawares and stick its wicked teeth into is fine. *(he laughs coldly)* I know how to deal with animals and humans. *(pause)* Some of that brute's slobber has got onto my clean waistcoat. You must excuse me. *(he bows to* **Marian**. *The doorbell rings)* Ah, you have another visitor, Percival.

SIR PERCIVAL My lawyer, Merriman, I expect.

Count Fosco *goes out as* **Merriman** *enters. He is middle-aged and drab in appearance.*

MERRIMAN Sir Percival, how do you do? *(the two men shake hands)* If I may, a word in private.

The two men walk to the far corner of the library and speak in hushed tones. **48** *Marian picks up a book and pretends to read. She can hear the conversation.*

MERRIMAN Make your mind easy, Sir Percival. It all rests with Lady Glyde. She is to sign her name in the presence of a witness. She is then to put her finger on the seal and say "I deliver this as my art and deed." Otherwise, the bills...

SIR PERCIVAL *(raises his voice)* Damn the bills! She will sign, I *(cough)* shall see to that. Come Merriman, we must leave soon.

Sir Percival and Merriman exit. Marian puts down her book and looks after them. Laura enters. Marian and Laura embrace.

MARIAN Laura dear, I have something to tell you. I fear that Sir Percival is in need of money and will ask you to sign a bill so that he can get some of yours.

LAURA *(looking resigned)* I feared as much. Somebody has heavy claims upon him.

Count Fosco comes back in unnoticed.

MARIAN You must sign nothing. Sir Percival does not want your love; he is after your money.

Count Fosco approaches the sisters, who look up and see him.

COUNT FOSCO My dear Lady Glyde and the charming Miss Halcombe. *(he kisses Marian's hand again, though she tries to pull it away from him)* Do you think your husband's cough is worse, Lady Glyde? And how thin he has become.

LAURA No, no, he is well, I believe. Thank you for your concern.

COUNT FOSCO Forgive me for leaving you, but I must feed my canaries. Fine birds are they not? They are well trained and well looked after, totally in my power. If I did not look after them, they would die. I have a certain way with birds. They all love me. *(he chuckles)* I believe they trust me!

He walks to the other end of the library, mimes letting canaries out of a cage and allowing them to fly round the room, then calling them back to land again on his hand.

LAURA Marian, do not take that man into your confidence.

MARIAN Have you reason to dislike the Count?

LAURA *(her voice rising as she watches **Fosco**)* On the contrary, he was all kindness to me in Italy. He has checked my husband's outbreaks of temper several times. Perhaps I dislike him because he has so much more power over my husband than I have. All I know is that I do dislike him.

MARIAN Hush, dear Laura. Do not make an enemy of that man, I beg of you. He is a powerful figure, I fear.

*Sir Percival enters. He beckons **Fosco** to him and together they approach the sisters. **Sir Percival** has some papers in his hand.*

SIR PERCIVAL Do *(cough)* sit down, dear Laura, and Miss Halcombe too. I *(cough)* need you to sign a mere trifle of a document, Laura.

*Marian and Laura sit down at a table. **Sir Percival** produces a pen and hands this to **Laura**.*

SIR PERCIVAL I shall need two witnesses. Miss Halcombe, if you would be so good. And... Count Fosco.

COUNT FOSCO Of course, delighted to be of service.

MARIAN You may rely upon me as a witness.

SIR PERCIVAL *(to **Laura**, handing her the papers)* Sign there.

LAURA What is it I am to sign?

SIR PERCIVAL I have no *(cough)* time to explain. Besides, if I had time, you wouldn't understand. It is purely a formal document. Come! Come! Sign your name.

LAURA I ought to know what I am signing.

SIR PERCIVAL Nonsense! What have women to do with business? I tell you again, you wouldn't understand.

LAURA Uncle's lawyer, Mr Gilmore, always explained business first. I…

SIR PERCIVAL I dare say he did. He was your servant and I am your husband. I am not obliged to explain anything. Do as I say!

LAURA If my signature pledges me to anything, surely I have some claim to know what the pledge is?

SIR PERCIVAL You do not! *(cough)* You must trust me, Laura, as I am your husband. *(he notices **Laura** shaking her head, loses his temper and snarls at her)* You do not trust me?

COUNT FOSCO *(stepping forward, speaking softly and putting his hands on **Sir Percival**'s shoulders)* Control your temper, Percival. Lady Glyde is right.

PERCIVAL *(grabs the papers from the table and stuffs them under his arm)* Damnation!

COUNT FOSCO Percival! Be good enough to remember you are in the presence of ladies. *(his hands are still on **Sir Percival**'s shoulders and slowly he forces him to sit down)* Percival, I am advising you for your own good. Give Lady Glyde time. You are a busy man today. Can the business of the signature be put off until tomorrow? Yes or no?

SIR PERCIVAL *(snaps)* Yes. *(he glares at **Laura**)* If you do not sign tomorrow…

Sir Percival storms offstage.

MARIAN Thank you, Count Fosco.

FOSCO *(bows)* At your service. You have just seen Percival at his worst. As his old friend, I apologise for him. I promise he will not act in the same disgraceful way tomorrow. Now, please excuse me, I must make friends with Percival's hunting dogs.

He bows again and exits.

Laura Oh Marian, I fear there is much we should know about my husband. *(she puts one hand to her head)* I must take some fresh air – my poor head aches, aches, aches. It will burst if I do not escape from the house for a while.

Marian *(putting an arm around **Laura**'s shoulders)* My poor, darling sister! Has marriage been a strain, Laura?

Laura I once asked my husband, if I died would he build a tomb for me?

Marian What did he say, Laura?

Laura He laughed. He said if he did build a tomb, it would be with my money. You must thank God for your poverty, Marian. Now I must calm myself. I will take a walk in the grounds. *(**Marian** makes a move as if to go with her)* No, dear Marian, I must be by myself. What shall we do? Oh, for a friend to help us – one we could really trust!

*She leaves the library to go outside. **Marian** watches her leave, then exits.*

Scene Two

*The grounds at Blackwater Park. **Laura** approaches a woman in white, who turns around: it is **Anne Catherick**. Slow, atmospheric music plays during the conversation between **Anne** and **Laura**. The two women stop and gaze at each other for several seconds. **Anne** looks pale and exhausted.*

Laura *(shocked)* You are so like me!

Anne *(reaching out with one hand to touch **Laura**'s face)* You have not got your mother's face. You are fair and she was dark. But her heart, Miss Fairlie, was the heart of an angel.

Laura Why do you call me Miss Fairlie?

Anne Because I love the name Fairlie and hate the name of Glyde.

Laura I thought that perhaps you might not know I am married.

24

ANNE I am here because you are married. I am here to make atonement to you, before I meet your mother in the world beyond the grave. Your mother was more of a mother to me than my own, more of a mother than Sir Percival's was to him. I have risked being shut up again in the madhouse – all for your sake.

LAURA *(astonished)* For my sake?

ANNE *(glances round nervously)* Why did I let you marry Sir Percival? Why did I lack the courage to warn you. Oh my fear – my mad, miserable, wicked fear! Wouldn't you be afraid of a man who had shut you up in a madhouse and who would again if he could?

LAURA Are you afraid still? Surely you would not be here if you were afraid still.

ANNE Can't you guess why I am not afraid of him now? *(Laura shakes her head)* Look at me again – I'm ill. I'm dying. I want to undo all I can of the harm I once did. Will your mother forgive me, when we meet in the next world? Surely she can? He has a secret. Sir Percival has a secret. You shall threaten him with the secret and frighten him. The secret will undo him, bring him down. Yes, he has a terrible secret. *(she hears footsteps)* Someone is coming. I must go!

LAURA *(holds onto **Anne's** arm)* The secret – don't go! Tell me the secret!

ANNE *(pulling away from **Laura**)* Not now, we are not alone – we are watched. Come here tomorrow, by yourself, at the same time. Remember… tomorrow!

*Anne hurries offstage. **Count Fosco** enters.*

COUNT FOSCO Ah, Lady Glyde. Out alone in the grounds? All by yourself?

LAURA I needed a walk. My head ached fit to burst.

COUNT FOSCO Ah, quite so. Come and indulge me: see my canaries. They sing so beautifully that you will feel relaxed in their company, my dear Lady Glyde.

He takes her arm and they exit together.

Scene Three

Marian is in her bedroom.

MARIAN *(to audience)* Laura told me everything. I was convinced Sir Percival Glyde had a secret, a terrible secret that only Anne Catherick could tell us. I was determined to find out. I decided that Laura must meet Anne Catherick at the boat house after lunch, as she had done the day before. The Count was feeding his canaries and Sir Percival was taking his customary afternoon nap. I decided to follow my sister. But Anne Catherick was not there. Nor would I ever now see her on this earth. *(Sir Percival and Count Fosco enter. They appear to have been arguing)* Later that night, in my own room, I heard Sir Percival and Count Fosco talking in whispers outside. *(mimes her actions as she describes them)* I crept from my bed and climbed out of the window. I crawled along a narrow ledge, at some risk to myself, until I was above them. *(whispering)* I could hear almost every word.

Marian kneels down, listening from the ledge outside her bedroom window. The Count and Sir Percival are in heated discussion.

SIR PERCIVAL The devil take your restlessness!

COUNT FOSCO Ouf! How hot it is! And what a crisis!

SIR PERCIVAL There will be a storm. And the crisis *(cough)* is worse than you think. I need thousands, you need hundreds. Without *(cough)* money, we are both in a fair way to the dogs.

COUNT FOSCO And the only chance of obtaining money is with the help of your dear wife.

SIR PERCIVAL I did not marry her for love, Fosco. *(he laughs)* I love only myself!

COUNT FOSCO Your wife will never sign the papers because you appear suspicious, Percival. You deserve to fail and you have failed. Tell me in plain words, do you want my help?

SIR PERCIVAL Yes, badly enough. We need a great deal of money. The interest from my wife's money is not enough for our dual expenses.

Count Fosco And the uncle, Mr Fairlie?

Sir Percival A selfish fool who bores everyone about the state of his health.

Count Fosco Men of that sort, Percival, live long and marry when you least expect it. You will have your wife's money only when she dies.

Sir Percival Yes... But Fosco...

Count Fosco I could help you in this little matter.

Marian gasps and the men look up sharply, then continue.

Sir Percival There is more to it than you know of, though. *(cough)*

Count Fosco If you can tell me without incriminating yourself, then tell me.

Sir Percival Today I have done my best to find a certain Anne Catherick and I have failed. She knows a secret that could ruin me. I believe she has been trying to communicate with my wife. Anne Catherick is just mad enough to be shut up in an asylum, and just sane enough to ruin me when she's at large.

Count Fosco Serious, indeed – as serious as the money troubles. *(he lets his canaries out of their cage and strokes them as they sit on his fingers. Marian is getting stiff squatting down trying to hear. She shifts her position and the men hear her and look around to see what made the noise. They hear and see nothing and relax again after a few seconds)* Pray describe Miss Catherick to me.

Sir Percival *(starting to lose his temper)* What the devil...! *(Fosco gives Sir Percival a look and holds up one hand. Percival calms down)* Very well. I can describe her most simply in saying imagine my wife, after a bad illness, with a touch of something wrong in her head, and there is Anne Catherick for you. It is part of her madness always to wear white.

Count Fosco Are Lady Glyde and Anne Catherick related, Percival?

Sir Percival *(uneasily)* Certainly not!

Count Fosco *(laughs)* Said too hastily, Percival! *(putting the canaries back into the cage)* Trust me, Percival. I have my projects and my plans here in my big head. You shall pay those bills and find Anne Catherick – my sacred word of honour on it. Enough for tonight, Percival. Sleep easily. *(**Sir Percival** exits. To the canaries)* Come kiss me, my pretties! And as for you, my little white canary, soon you will sing us your sweet song and make all our troubles fly away – as you never will...

*He kisses the bird on his finger, returns it to the cage and shuts it. As he does so, there is the sound of thunder and rain. **Fosco** goes to look out of the window, reaches out a hand, feels rain, locks the window and exits. Meanwhile, **Marian** tries to shelter her head from the rain with her hands. She struggles back along the ledge, starting to shiver. She climbs back in through her window and collapses. Blackout.*

Scene Four

***Marian's** bedroom. It is morning. The sound of birdsong. The **maid** comes in. **Marian** lies collapsed on the floor, fully dressed. The **maid** shakes **Marian**, who does not move, then goes to the door and screams. **Sir Percival** and **Count Fosco** come running.*

Sir Percival Whatever is the matter?

Maid Beggin' your pardon, your lordship. Miss Halcombe is unwell. She is all sweat and delirium.

Count Fosco Allow me to attend to Miss Halcombe, I have some knowledge in these matters.

*He goes into **Marian's** room and shuts the door. **Laura** enters.*

Maid Lady Glyde, Lady Glyde, your sister is unwell.

Laura Marian unwell? But she is usually so robust, so strong.

*Count Fosco comes out of **Marian's** room.*

Count Fosco We must call a doctor at once. Miss Halcombe has the scarlet fever. Lady Glyde, I must ask to stay away from your sister and not to risk infection.

LAURA *(starts to cry)* Is it…? Is she…? Will she…?

SIR PERCIVAL *(unsympathetic)* Yes, the scarlet fever is life-threatening. *(he coughs)* She may die – we must be prepared.

COUNT FOSCO My dear Percival, do not alarm Lady Glyde. A woman of Miss Halcombe's robust health…

LAURA Oh, oh…

*Laura faints. While she is unconscious, **Fosco** and **Sir Percival** carry **Marian** offstage.*

Scene Five

*Mr Fairlie's room at Limmeridge House. **Count Fosco** comes in.*

COUNT FOSCO Sir, I come from Blackwater Park. I enter this room and see you are a sufferer. Alas, I must increase your suffering by bringing you sad news.

MR FAIRLIE Must I really hear it? *(Fosco nods)* Please break it gently. Anyone dead?

COUNT FOSCO Dead! Your English calm terrifies me. In the name of heaven, what have I done to make you think that? No, no one is dead.

MR FAIRLIE *(coldly)* Inexpressibly relieved, I am sure, to hear no one is dead. Anybody ill?

COUNT FOSCO Yes, Mr Fairlie, somebody is ill.

MR FAIRLIE Grieved, I am sure. Which of them is it?

COUNT FOSCO To my profound sorrow, Miss Halcombe. She has a fever.

MR FAIRLIE *(horrified)* Fever? Good God, is it infectious?

COUNT FOSCO Not at present. I bear yet more sad news. I fear that Lady Glyde and Sir Percival are experiencing some… difficulties. A temporary separation is the only solution. No other house except Limmeridge House can receive her and avoid scandal. I myself will offer her hospitality in London overnight. She needs only your invitation to do so. *(pause)* She needs only your invitation to do so. *(pause)* And I will stay until I get it.

MR FAIRLIE *(waves at his pen and paper, which **Fosco** immediately gives him. He speaks as he writes)* "Dearest Laura, please come and stay with me whenever you like. Break the journey by sleeping in London at Count Fosco's house if you wish. Grieved to hear of Marian. Ever affectionately yours" *(he signs a big signature, but feebly as if exhausted. He blots the letter and holds it out to **Fosco**, who snatches and reads it. **Mr Fairlie** closes his eyes)* Much obliged, I am sure for your kind interference.

Fosco carefully folds the letter, tucks it into a pocket and exits.

Scene Six

The corridor outside Marian's bedroom at Blackwater Park.

LAURA It has been three days now – I must see my sister. You are keeping something from me. *(pause)* Is she dead?

SIR PERCIVAL *(gloomily)* She has… gone. *(he indicates her empty bedroom)*

LAURA *(very afraid)* Dead?

SIR PERCIVAL Her body was taken on a train last night to Limmeridge House, accompanied by Count Fosco.

LAURA I must be with her as she is buried! I insist!

SIR PERCIVAL Please do not distress yourself, Laura. Here is a letter from your uncle inviting you to follow. *(he holds out a letter to **Laura**, who takes and reads it)*

LAURA "Dearest Laura, please come whenever you like. Break the journey by sleeping in London at Count Fosco's house… Grieved to hear of Marian. Ever affectionately yours, Frederick Fairlie." I must leave at once. *(**Laura** exits)*

Scene Seven

Laura, dressed for travelling, is in a railway carriage. Sound effects of a 46 *steam train whistling, slowing down and braking as it comes into a station. A guard appears in the corridor.*

GUARD *(calling out)* Waterloo Station. All change here. Waterloo Station.

*Fosco enters. He comes up to the train compartment and opens the door, giving **Laura** his hand to help her out. He keeps hold of her hand and starts to drag her along with him. Blackout.*

Scene Eight

*A room somewhere in London. There are shadows across the stage suggesting a barred window. **Fosco** stands in the middle of the stage and beckons.*

*As if in a trance, **Laura** and **Anne Catherick** enter from either side, walking very slowly towards each other. When they are within reach of each other, **Fosco** holds up his hand and they stop, still looking at each other.*

*He points at **Laura** and she takes off her bonnet and cloak. He then points at **Anne**, who takes off her white veil and jacket. **Fosco** gestures and **Laura** and **Anne** exchange clothes. Each puts on the clothes that the other has taken off. There is the sound of a canary singing as they do this.*

*Fosco then points at **Laura**, now wearing **Anne**'s white veil and jacket and points to the side of the stage from which **Anne** came. **Laura** walks slowly towards it and as she does so we hear police whistles and footsteps.*

MAN FROM THE ASYLUM There she is – all in white, just as I described! This is the woman who escaped from my asylum. Seize her!

POLICEMAN Right away, sir!

*The two men grab **Laura** and march her offstage. **Fosco** points at **Anne**, who is wearing **Laura**'s bonnet and cloak and beckons her to him and takes her arm. They walk offstage together.*

ACT THREE
Scene One

WALTER *(to audience)* I was back in London – back from Central America. I had survived death by Indians, death by disease, death by drowning. I was home!

He remains on stage during the following scene.

Scene Two

The London apartment of **Count Fosco**, *a comfortable study with a desk in it.* **Fosco** *is seated, reading. There is a knock at the door.*

COUNT FOSCO Come in.

The **maid** *enters.*

MAID Sir.

COUNT FOSCO Lady Glyde will be arriving soon. She was on her way to Limmeridge, but she has been taken ill. She is quite poorly, I am afraid. Make a bed up for her, will you?

MAID Yes, sir.

The doorbell rings. The maid opens the door to **Anne Catherick**, *dressed in* **Laura**'s *clothes. She staggers in through the front door, gives a scream of fear and collapses.*

MAID Count Fosco! Count Fosco!

COUNT FOSCO *(leaping from his chair)* Whatever is the matter?

MAID The lady is dead, sir.

Fosco bends down and feels for a pulse.

COUNT FOSCO It was her heart. Lady Glyde was never strong.

He looks at the **maid**, *with a cold expression that silences further questions.*

Scene Three

The graveyard at Limmeridge.

WALTER *(to audience)* When I heard of my love's death, I knew I had to return to Limmeridge, to the place were I first met dear Laura.

*He goes to look at **Mrs Fairlie**'s grave. Two veiled women walk towards **Walter**. One lifts her veil. It is **Marian Halcombe**.*

MARIAN *(reads the inscription on the gravestone)* "Sacred to the memory of Laura, Lady Glyde."

*The other woman lifts her veil. It is **Laura**. She is stooped and looks weak and ill.*

WALTER Laura…

52

Blackout.

Scene Four

Walter's lodgings in Limmeridge.*

LAURA Yes, Mr Hartright, I still live. The world thinks me dead and indeed I am dead to the world. My uncle and the servants fail to recognise me. I think Percival has bribed the servants, and I look more like poor dead Anne since my time in the asylum.

MARIAN Laura has taken on the disguise of Anne Catherick. You must help us, Walter. Help Laura find her true identity, or Sir Percival has made a pauper of her.

WALTER How? What has happened?

MARIAN Tell him, Laura.

LAURA Count Fosco met me on the train from Blackwater Park. He appeared kind and courteous. He seemed to care for me, although I should have known better. He was worried for my health, so he took me into his house in St John's Wood. He gave me a drink … Oh, it is all so dreadful. *(she sits down sobbing at the memory)*

33

WALTER Please don't distress yourself, Laura.

MARIAN When Laura awoke, she was in an asylum wearing Anne Catherick's clothes – the very clothes that Anne had been wearing when she escaped from the asylum! The nurses had been warned by Count Fosco that Anne Catherick believed she was Lady Glyde. No matter how poor Laura protested, the truth about her identity was taken as a sign of her madness. When I recovered from my illness, I could not believe my sister was dead. I remembered Anne had escaped from an asylum in Hampshire. I wanted to speak to her. Imagine my shock when I visited the asylum to find my sister there!

LAURA And mine when I looked up to see my sister, whom I had believed dead, was there before me, and in such a place!

MARIAN I did the only thing I could do in such conditions. I sold everything I owned and went back to the asylum.

Lights dim. Demonic laughter. **Nurses** *encircle* **Laura**, *menacing and confusing her, then exit one by one until one is left.* **Marian** *watches, then beckons the remaining nurse over. She hands the nurse a pile of notes. The* **nurse** *counts them and puts them hastily in her pocket, looking around as if afraid of being watched. She creeps back to* **Laura** *and, putting her finger to her lips, leads her by the hand.* **Laura** *is reluctant to go with her at first. They tip-toe over to* **Marian**. **Laura** *rushes towards* **Marian** *as soon as she sees her and they embrace, as the* **nurse** *runs off. Then they too run off, hand in hand, looking around them, being careful not to be followed. The scene moves back into* **Walter**'s *lodgings, as the lights come back up.*

MARIAN So Lord Percival and Count Fosco have twenty thousand pounds to spend, and poor Laura is penniless.

WALTER And Anne Catherick lies in a grave sacred to the memory of Lady Glyde.

MARIAN Exactly so! She is next to our mother. Anne in some way has what she wanted.

WALTER May she rest in peace. *(pause)* But we must prove that Laura is Lady Glyde!

MARIAN Promise me one thing, Walter: that if you ever have the chance, you will crush Count Fosco. Begin with the Count – for my sake, begin with the Count.

WALTER I will do everything in my power, Marian. But we must begin where there is best chance of success: with Sir Percival.

MARIAN How can we get Sir Percival to tell the world the truth?

LAURA We must show the world what he really is. Anne Catherick told me he had a secret. She would have revealed that secret, because she knew it too, if Count Fosco had not disturbed us that day in Blackwater Park. Oh, the thought of it makes me feel quite faint. *(she breaks down in tears)*

MARIAN You have had a frightful ordeal, Laura. You must sit down. *(she helps **Laura** to a chair)*

WALTER *(to **Marian**)* She is not strong. We must travel to London as soon as possible. We can leave Laura in my London flat, attended by my mother, then return to Blackwater Park. I mean to talk to Mrs Catherick. She must know something of what happened to her daughter – how she ended as she did.

MARIAN She knows one thing: who Anne's father is. Anne never told us that… if she even knew.

Scene Five

*Mrs **Catherick**'s simple kitchen. She is sitting by a window clothed in black. There is a knock on the door. **Walter** and **Marian** enter.*

MRS CATHERICK You have come here to speak to me about my daughter. Have you come to tell me she is dead?

WALTER *(startled)* Ah… yes, I have.

MRS CATHERICK Why?

WALTER *(astonished)* Why?

MRS CATHERICK Yes, why? What interest do you have in me, or in her? How do you come to know anything about my daughter?

WALTER By chance, I met her on the night she escaped from the asylum, and I assisted her in reaching a place of safety.

MRS CATHERICK You did very wrong.

WALTER I am sorry to hear her mother say so.

MRS CATHERICK If you have no other motive in coming here other than to inform me of her death, I shall wish you both good morning. I suppose your information justifies me going into mourning, though as you see, there is not much alteration necessary in my dress.

MARIAN We have another motive. Your daughter's death has been made a pretext for inflicting serious injury on a person who is very dear to us. Two men have to my knowledge been involved in doing that wrong. One of them is Sir Percival Glyde.

MRS CATHERICK *(showing little emotion)* Ah! I am beginning to understand. You have got a grudge of you own against Sir Percival and you want my help in bringing about his downfall.

MARIAN We believe Sir Percival has wronged you too, many years ago. Mrs Catherick, was Sir Percival Anne's father?

MRS CATHERICK *(furious)* How dare you talk to me about Anne's father! How dare you say who was her father, or who wasn't! Do you think I am a lost woman who had an affair with Sir Percival? Is that what you think? Ha! You are wrong. I am not a woman who has lost her character, even if my husband did desert me years ago. He was wrong to do that, wrong!

WALTER Yet you are afraid of Sir Percival. He is a powerful man, a baronet, and has a high position in the world. He is the descendant of a great family.

MRS CATHERICK *(bitter and contemptuous)* Yes, indeed! A great family – especially by the mother's side. Now go – and never come back!

WALTER I'll come back when I have news of Sir Percival.

MRS CATHERICK There is no news of Sir Percival that I shall want – except the news of his death. Good-bye!

*Marian and **Walter** leave **Mrs Catherick**'s house. The lights go down on **Mrs Catherick** and up on **Marian** and **Walter** downstage.*

Scene Six

Walter and Marian are outside Blackwater Church.

MARIAN We know Sir Percival's father and mother must have married here at Blackwater Church, before Mrs Catherick was born. We must look at the church records. There will just be time before night falls.

Marian does not wait for him to reply, but goes to the church door, which she tries to open. It is too stiff for her.

WALTER Allow me, Marian.

He too struggles with the door, and eventually manages to open it. They go inside. The lighting changes to soft colours, to represent stained glass. The parish clerk enters.

CLERK May I assist you?

WALTER We need to look at church records from a long while ago.

CLERK Ah, yes, follow me. *(he leads them around a series of obstacles)* We might be tidier, mightn't we, madam?

MARIAN What's in those packing cases?

CLERK Why, bits of old wood-carvings from the church, all of them broken and worm-eaten and crumbling to dust at the edges. We were hoping to send them to London to get them repaired. We got so far as packing them up, but then the money fell short. These packing cases have been littering the place for a good few years now and there they'll stop as long as the nails hold them together. Dry as anything, they are. Now what were you looking for? We must hurry if you are to find what you seek before dark.

He produces a heavy book.

MARIAN Eighteen hundred and four – or further back, perhaps?

WALTER *(takes the book)* Surely, a book as valuable as this ought to be locked up?

CLERK Never has been, sir. We're honest folk in Hampshire, sir. Besides, there's a copy of it kept by a gentleman in town. Do catch up with me later, when you've had your search, sir, *(he bows)* madam.

*The clerk goes out. Silence as **Walter** and **Marian** turn over the pages of the large book and look over each one.*

MARIAN *(pointing at the book)* Walter, here, look! Look at this page!

WALTER *(reading)* Sir Felix Glyde... to Cecilia Jane Elster... only daughter of Patrick Elster... It all appears to be in order, Marian.

MARIAN Look again, Walter. Look at the writing. The entry is written very small at the bottom of the page. It looks as if it has been added in different handwriting. I am sure the marriage never took place. It is a forgery! Percival should never have inherited an estate. He is an impostor! That is the secret: he is not a gentleman, at all. His mother never married Sir Felix Glyde!

WALTER How can we prove this?

MARIAN We must check the copy that the clerk mentioned. We must do so at once!

*As **Walter** and **Marian** are carefully replacing the ledger, **Sir Percival** comes into the church. It has been getting darker and darker throughout the scene. He is carrying a torch and an iron bar.*

SIR PERCIVAL Fools! *(**Walter** and **Marian** jump)* Did you think you could find this place without my knowledge? I have had this place watched for months. As soon as you arrived here, I knew. You know my secret, but you will die for it. *(coughs)*

MARIAN You have brought about the death of your daughter, Anne Catherick, and now you would destroy us.

SIR PERCIVAL My dear Miss Halcombe, for once your intelligence fails you. Mrs Catherick was my accomplice, not my lover. *(he sneers)* Have you never wondered at the likeness between Anne and Laura? Anne's father was Mr Fairlie, father to your sister Laura. He liked his little flings, even if he was a gentleman.

Marian *(shocked)* No!

Walter If what you say is true, how did you become involved with Mrs Catherick?

Sir Percival She had discovered my secret in the church records. When her husband left her after discovering who Anne's father was, Mrs Catherick came to me in need of assistance. We reached a deal. *(cough)* I paid her to keep quiet all those years, but she foolishly told her daughter our little secret.

Walter And that's why you had Anne locked up in an asylum.

Sir Percival Indeed. She could not keep a secret. Mrs Catherick had no love for the daughter who had lost her her husband and her reputation. She was happy to see Anne out of the way, so long as she had enough money to live respectably. As for Mr Fairlie, I was prepared to keep his secret so long as he arranged my marriage to Laura Fairlie. I needed her money *(he laughs)* and now I have it all!

He uses the bar as a stave and swings at **Walter***, who ducks.* **Sir Percival** *trips over with the force of the blow. The torch falls to the ground.*

Walter Quick, Marian, out!

They run out and there is the sound of a heavy door swinging shut. **Sir Percival** *tries to open the door, which is stuck. He struggles. The lighting changes to represent flames. Sounds of a fire raging.*

Sir Percival Help! The bolt has broken! Help! HELP!

Walter *(outside the church)* He may be a villain, but I must rescue him!

Walter *fights against the flames. The* **clerk** *appears and tries to hold* **Walter** *back.*

Walter Let me go! I can't let a man die!

Clerk Back, sir! The smoke will overcome you! The packing cases must have caught fire.

WALTER There's a man inside!

There are horrific screams from inside the church. Sounds of crashing timbers. **Walter** *breaks free from the* **clerk***'s grasp.*

CLERK Too late, sir, I fear the roof has collapsed!

Walter *sinks to his knees. Blackout.*

Scene Seven

The following day. **Marian** *and* **Walter** *are in the churchyard at Blackwater, looking at the smoking ruins of the church.*

MARIAN You did your best to save him, Walter.

WALTER We are still no nearer to proving Laura's identity. I was about to force Sir Percival's hand. Now we have no hope, no proof. She is doomed to poverty.

MARIAN There is one man who can prove who Laura is: Count Fosco!

WALTER But how? We need some more information about Fosco. *(pause)* I have an Italian friend, Professor Pesca. He has always offered me his help, as I once saved him from drowning. With your permission, Marian, I shall write to him and ask if he knows the Count, as a fellow Italian.

MARIAN We should try any road that is open to us. But I must return to London and see how dear Laura is.

WALTER To London, then. It's time I met the Count on his home ground.

Scene Eight

A street in London. **Walter** *is walking along with* **Pesca***. The street is busy. There is a fruit stand. A beggar with a little dog is asking passers-by for money.* **Walter** *gives her a coin as he passes her.*

WALTER Pesca, if you know anything at all of this man, it would be of great service to me.

PESCA Right-all-right. Anything for a friend.

WALTER There he is.

Walter waits in the shadows. ***Pesca*** *goes to the fruit stand, and inspects the oranges.* ***Fosco*** *enters, carrying a pastry in a paper bag. He sees the dog.*

COUNT FOSCO *(to the dog)* My poor little brute! You look hungry. In the sacred name of humanity, I offer you some lunch! *(he gives the dog a bit of his pastry)*

BEGGAR Please sir, I'm hungry too. Can you spare a farthing?

Fosco shrugs, pats the dog and walks away. He stops at the fruit stall. He sees ***Pesca****, who pretends not to notice him.* ***Fosco*** *stares at* ***Pesca*** *for a few seconds, then backs away and exits in a hurry.* ***Walter*** *steps forward from his hiding place.*

WALTER Well?

PESCA The big fat man is a stranger to me. Is he famous? Why do you point him out?

WALTER He is a countryman of yours. His name is Count Fosco. Do you know that name?

PESCA Not I, Walter, neither the name nor the man is known to me.

WALTER And yet, Pesca, when the Count saw you just now I am certain that he knew you. And what's more, that he feared you.

PESCA Deuce-what-the-deuce! How can I help you, Walter, when I don't know the man?

WALTER Pesca, I beg of you, look back into your own life before you left Italy. You have never mentioned the reasons for your departure to me and I don't inquire into them now. I only ask you to consult your recollections and to say if they suggest to you no past cause for the terror which the first sight of you produced in that man.

The stage begins to go dark around them, leaving the two men in a spotlight.

PESCA *(looks horrified, and trembles)* Walter! You don't know what you ask. On your heart and soul, is there no other way to get to the man but through me?

WALTER There is no other way.

PESCA *(whispering)* My next words, as true as the good God is above us, will put my life into your hands. I left Italy for political reasons. You have heard, Walter, of the political societies that are hidden in every great city in Europe? (***Walter** nods*) To one of those societies I belonged and belong still. We are warned, if we betray the Brotherhood that we will die by the hand of a stranger. I joined such a society – the little, easy, cheerful man you know who would hardly lift up his handkerchief to strike the fly that buzzes around his face! We are identified in the Brotherhood by a secret mark, which we all bear, and which lasts for life. *(**Pesca** rolls up one sleeve and reveals a mark on his arm)* It is possible that the fat man, who you showed me, knows me in connection with the Brotherhood. If it is so, he is so altered or so disguised that I do not know him. Walter, I put my life in your hands. If anyone else discovers what I have told you, I am a dead man.

WALTER *(clasping **Pesca**'s shaking hand in his own to reassure him)* You shall never repent the trust you have placed in me.

Blackout.

Scene Nine

***Fosco**'s house. **Fosco** is letting his canaries out of their cage. There are signs of packing all round the room, such as boxes and clothes trailing out of suitcases.*

COUNT FOSCO Come on, out on my finger, my pret-pret-pretties! Come out and hop! Come out and fly! Soon we must leave on a long journey.

*He watches the birds fly around the room. **Walter** enters. **Fosco** turns to him.*

WALTER I am fortunate to find you here tonight. You seem to be on the point of taking a journey. I have come on a matter of life and death.

COUNT FOSCO So you know why I am leaving London? Tell me the reason, if you please.

WALTER I can do better than that. I can show you the reason.

Walter steps up to Fosco and pulls back his sleeve, revealing a mark like that on Pesca's arm.

COUNT FOSCO *(coolly)* I am thinking whether I shall add to the disorder in this room by scattering your brains about the fireplace.

WALTER I have a friend who bears a similar mark on his arm to that on yours. He is a man whom I have every reason to depend on and you have every reason to fear. Unless he hears from me before dawn tomorrow, he will open a letter that I have left with him.

Pause.

COUNT FOSCO What do you want of me?

WALTER I demand a full confession in writing of the conspiracy.

COUNT FOSCO *(with a dramatic laugh)* I accept your terms. I, Fosco, will write you a remarkable document.

He sits at a desk and scribbles frantically, throwing bits of paper all over the floor over his shoulder as he writes, getting more and more frantic. Walter watches him. Eventually Fosco stops writing, gathers up the papers and gives them to Walter with a bow.

COUNT FOSCO Today we meet as gentlemen. Next time we meet it will be different. You are cleverer than I thought. I shall enjoy destroying a worthy opponent.

Walter takes the papers, bows and leaves. Fosco lets the last canaries out of their cage.

COUNT FOSCO I will let you have your freedom now. Go, my pretties, go!

*Fosco freezes. There is the sound of a gunshot. **Fosco** falls. As the lights go down, there is a voice-over of a paper boy calling.*

PAPER BOY Read all about the latest gang-land murder! Corpse of Italian count found in the River Thames! Extra, extra – read all about it!

Scene Ten

*The graveyard at Limmeridge. **Marian**, **Laura** and **Walter** are all in mourning, dressed in black.*

LAURA I fear that there really was something wrong with my uncle.

WALTER At least he died after admitting that you were alive and had been treated cruelly by Sir Percival and Count Fosco. Justice has been done: you have inherited Limmeridge House and been restored to your true identity.

MARIAN *(to **Laura** and **Walter**)* Walter, you have been our truest friend. I was wrong to part you and Laura. You have each other and you must marry. You shall marry, I order it! Please forgive me, Walter!

*Marian takes hold of **Walter**'s hand and **Laura**'s and joins them. **Walter** and **Laura** embrace. Once again, **Laura** puts on a white veil. She takes **Walter**'s hand and, followed by **Marian**, they begin to exit to the sound of wedding bells. The lights dim and once more the audience sees the figure of the **woman in white** approaching the gravestone of **Mrs Fairlie**. She kneels and embraces the headstone. **Walter** remains on stage, and watches her from a distance.*

WALTER So the ghostly figure of Anne Catherick went down into the gloom. Like a shadow she first came to me in the loneliness of the night. Like a shadow, she passed away in the loneliness of the dead.

*He leaves the stage, leaving **Anne** in a spotlight. Blackout after a few seconds.*

THE END

Staging the play

The play is made up of 28 short scenes. To avoid lots of interruptions for scene changes, the play can be staged very simply. There is no need for a set; all the locations can be suggested with different arrangements of five chairs, a small table and simple props. At the beginning of the play, a chair is placed upstage (at the back of the stage) with its back towards the audience and draped with a white cloth. This represents Mrs Fairlie's grave in Limmeridge graveyard. The two indoor scenes 5 which follow in Act One (Scenes 3 and 4) are pre-set in different areas on the stage.

The chairs stay on stage throughout the play and are moved to 8, 9 different areas, as necessary. Try to use all the stage, setting up the different rooms in different places. Use plain wooden chairs if possible.

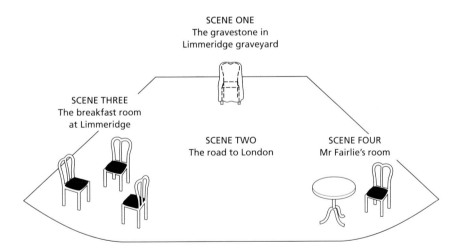

SCENE ONE
The gravestone in
Limmeridge graveyard

SCENE THREE
The breakfast room
at Limmeridge

SCENE TWO
The road to London

SCENE FOUR
Mr Fairlie's room

Use simple props to help indicate the different settings. Walter's suitcase opened on the floor tells us we are in his bedroom; a bowl of flowers on the side table gives us Marian's bedroom. And so on. Use as little as possible: let the audience use their imagination!

Stage set-up

Make a list of all the different scenes. Draw diagrams showing how you would set up each scene, using the chairs and table if you need them, and a minimum of props.

How can the audience tell the difference between Limmeridge House and Blackwater Park? Can you think of a prop that would help them?

SOUND EFFECTS

Sound effects are an effective and simple way of suggesting locations and creating the right atmosphere. You will need a steam train sound for Act 2, Scene 7; a canary singing would be an interesting and effective way of suggesting Fosco's house – with just the right edge of menace. Most of the sounds you might want are on BBC sound effect records, which are available in many libraries.

You might prefer to use music to create atmosphere, instead of sound effects. Decide on the mood you are looking for and ask your teacher or librarian to help you choose appropriate music.

Discussion

In groups What effects might you use to suggest the graveyard, or Walter's return to London (Act 3, Scene 1)? Make a list of other moments in the play when you would use sound effects, and decide what those effects would be.

COSTUMES

Think about whether it's practical to stage the play in full period costume – it can be expensive and difficult to arrange. As an alternative, you might want to use a basic, 'neutral' costume for all the actors, and then use hand props, for example: a cane for Sir Percival, to suggest his violent nature, a bonnet for Laura, a shawl for Anne Catherick. Again, the simplest ideas are often the best.

46

Work on and around the script

EXPLORING THE PLAY FURTHER

Imagine a photograph of Act Two, Scene One, in which Sir Percival **22** wants Laura to sign the papers. What would be the expression on the characters' faces? What would they have been thinking at the moment when the photo was taken?

 **Drama**

A. In groups Create a 'frozen picture' of the scene when Sir Percival Glyde wants Laura to sign the papers. Marian and Count Fosco are present. Arrange the actors so that what is going on in the scene would be clear to an observer who didn't know the play.

- Choose other moments in the story, and make a series of frozen pictures – a 'photo album' of key events.

- Choose one of the frozen pictures, and imagine what the characters are thinking. Give each actor one or two sentences to say which convey the character's thoughts, and perform these in front of the other groups.

- Improvise the scene which follows from the moment when the photo was taken.

B. In groups Select one of the following characters: Anne, Laura, Walter, Mrs Catherick, Sir Percival Glyde or Count Fosco. Take it in turns to prepare questions to ask each of the characters. This is called 'hot-seating'. The idea behind hot-seating is to help you to empathise with a character, to see things from that person's point of view. It gives you an opportunity to act in role, pretending you are a particular character to help understand their motives.

cont...

Here are some examples of the kind of questions you might ask:

"Walter, what did you think when the man told you Anne was mad?"

"Anne, why did you run away from Walter when you met him the second time? You could have told him the secret then."

"Marian, how did you feel when you told Walter he had to leave Limmeridge House? What were your feelings towards Walter at this time?"

"Sir Percival, what were your first impressions of Laura Fairlie and how could you treat her so badly?"

"Count Fosco, how did you feel when Walter confronted you in your London home? Why didn't you kill him?"

When you have done this in groups, volunteers come to the front of the class and the class asks their characters questions.

C. In pairs Improvise the scene between Sir Percival Glyde and Mr Merriman, the lawyer. This conversation must have taken place before Sir Percival tried to get Laura to sign the papers. Mr Merriman might have told Sir Percival that he owed money and had to find cash quickly or face bankruptcy. Make sure that you are clear about the events leading up to this incident.

Sir Percival and Count Fosco have several plans to overcome their shortage of money – Marian hears just one plan. Stay in character and improvise several scenes between the two as they discuss other ways of raising money.

✍ Writing

A. On your own Imagine you are a nurse charged with caring for Laura in the asylum. Write a report on Laura's condition when she arrives, and over the following months.

B. You are a reporter for a local newspaper. Write a front-page article about Count Fosco's mysterious death. Include interviews with the police and witnesses.

MELODRAMA

Melodrama was a popular form of theatre in the Victorian age. It portrayed, in sentimental and colourful style, the trials of virtuous people in the face of wickedness and adversity. The heroes often had to take terrible risks or undergo dangerous adventures at the risk of their lives. Always, just in time, the virtuous won through.

Wilkie Collins loved the theatre, and wrote a number of melodramas as a young man. His novels were strongly influenced by what he saw on stage. *The Woman in White*, with its saintly heroes and heroines and its wicked villains, is often described as a melodrama.

A scene from a melodrama (1868)

The Sailor's Return

The Sailor's Return is a parody of a typical melodrama of the period. On pages 50–51 is an outline of the scenes in the play, with all the information you will need to stage your own performance.

The melodrama itself, and each of the scenes, can be introduced by a large decorated placard carried onstage by one or two performers in appropriate costume. If there is a pianist, they should, like in silent films, accompany the action with appropriate music throughout the play.

1 The Happy Home

Polly's aged parents, poor but respectable, enter arm-in-arm. Father seats Mother carefully on a rustic bench, and then sits down himself. Meanwhile the pianist plays *Home Sweet Home*.

2 Polly and Her Friends

Pretty Polly, the heroine, skips on with her friends. They play happily together, perhaps throwing a ball, tossing flowers to each other or dancing. When Polly notices her father and mother nodding on the bench, she gestures to her companions to be quiet and waves them farewell. Then, with great affection, she adjusts her mother's shawl and sits at her feet. (Piano: *Polly Perkins of Paddington Green*)

3 Sailor Jack

Jack enters with considerable dash, and takes up a stance with his arms folded for the Sailor's Hornpipe. He dances a few steps, while Polly jumps to her feet and gazes at him with admiration. (Piano: *All the Nice Girls Love a Sailor*)

4 True Love

Polly holds out her arms to Jack, who goes on one knee and mimes "Will you marry me?" (hands to heart, then arms outstretched towards Polly). Polly mimes "What, me?" in innocent surprise (hands clasped, looking coy). Jack stands impulsively and holds out his arms to Polly. Polly nods shyly and they embrace.

Mother wakes up and looks on in delight, then wakens Father. Jack shakes Father by the hand. Father is still rather confused and uncertain of what has been happening.

Jack suddenly remembers that he is penniless. He mimes "I have no money", turning out his pocket and shaking his head. Polly and Mother are broken-hearted. Jack has a bright idea. He mimes "I will go away to sea to make my fortune". He gestures offstage and indicates that he will return to marry Polly. Jack bids Father and Mother a gallant farewell, and embraces Polly warmly. He leaves with his head held high. Polly collapses in grief and hides her head in her mother's lap. The family hold this position while the pianist plays sentimental music.

5 One Year Later *This placard can reverse to show the caption 'Hard Times'.*

Father, Mother and Polly have no money. Mother is ailing. Father helps her to lie down on a makeshift bed (or two chairs). Polly rushes off with her basket to seek food. Father is sunk in gloom and dabs his eyes with his handkerchief. (Piano: *Hearts and Flowers*)

6 Sir Jaspar, the Landlord

Suddenly there is a loud knocking at the door. The pianist plays doom-laden chords. Sir Jaspar, the villain, enters, twirling his moustache. He demands money for the mortgage, which he brandishes in front of Father – a huge scroll-like document bearing the word 'Mortgage'. Father indicates his empty pockets, and hides his head in his hands. Mother tries to sit up and plead with Sir Jaspar, but falls back fainting.

7 No Money for the Mortgage

Polly enters, in bare feet with an empty basket. Sir Jaspar shows her the mortgage and indicates that they must leave the house. Polly pleads with him to let them stay, going down on her knees, her hands clasped in entreaty. Sir Jaspar looks closely at Polly and leers. He paces up and down to consider the matter. Then he offers to tear up the mortgage if Polly will marry him. She is horrified and shrinks away from him, shaking her head. Sir Jaspar is furious and tries to seize her. Polly runs away from him and he pursues her round and round the stage while the pianist plays chase music. Mother and Father are helpless and horrified. The chase is fast and furious. Just as Sir Jaspar seizes Polly, she faints in his arms.

8 The Sailor's Return

Jack enters suddenly. He takes the situation in immediately. He challenges Sir Jaspar, who drops Polly unceremoniously and runs away. At last Jack corners the villain and there is a slow-motion struggle. Jack lands an uppercut and Sir Jaspar is defeated. Polly revives and mimes "My Hero!". Jack lifts her up and they embrace. Mother recovers and Father helps her to her feet. Jack shows the large bag of money he has earned and they are all united in happiness.

The pianist plays *The Wedding March* as the cast take a bow.

🎭 Drama

A. Make decorated placards and stage your own performance of *The Sailor's Return*. Perform in mime to musical accompaniment. If a piano is not available you could sing, use percussion or recorded music.

B. Write a short script for a spoken version of the scene where Sir Jaspar demands money from Polly's family. Perform your different versions in groups.

👀 Discussion

As a class

- Can you see any similarities between *The Woman in White* and *The Sailor's Return*?

- Are there moments in *The Woman in White* that you think are melodramatic (for example, when Walter meets Laura, veiled, in the graveyard, Act 3, Scene 3)?

🎭 Drama

In groups Choose and act out a scene from the play which you think is melodramatic. Discuss with the audience why you think it is melodramatic. Act out the scene in different ways to make it more or less melodramatic.

IDEAS FOR FURTHER WORK

✍ Writing

H

A. On your own Write an exchange of letters between two characters in the play at a particular moment in the story. For example:

- Walter and Pesca, after Walter leaves Limmeridge for South America

- Fosco and Sir Percival, after Fosco has abducted Laura

- Marian and Laura, after Laura's marriage to Sir Percival

cont...

B. EITHER: Write entries for Laura's diary, from the time of her first meeting with Walter to the period after her marriage to Sir Percival. H

OR: Choose another character and write diary entries covering a period in the story.

Radio documentary

In groups Imagine you are a journalist looking back at the events in the story years later. Work in groups to prepare a short documentary, using a tape recorder if one is available. Take turns to be a radio interviewer. Interview some of the characters, who will now be quite old. Who will you interview and what questions will you ask?

From novel to playscript

A recent TV adaptation of *The Woman in White* opens with a view of a graveyard and haunting music. Marian speaks in voice-over:

"Bad dreams always come back again like unwanted friends and last night I found myself in Limmeridge churchyard. Normally, people who are dead stay dead, just as, normally, it is the criminals who are locked up rather than the victims. But then, there was nothing normal about what happened to us, except perhaps the beginning: that summer's day on Limmeridge lawn when we witnessed the fate of Laura's croquet ball; and that night, the arrival of a tutor to teach us drawing."

The scene cuts to Laura knocking a croquet ball through a greenhouse window, then to Walter alone on a platform, watching his train pull away. Cut to a lonely lane at night. A signpost indicates: "Limmeridge, three miles". Anne, dressed in white, appears from behind Walter, and puts her hand on his shoulder:

ANNE You don't suspect me of wrong do you, sir?

The novel begins, after a prologue (an introduction written by the author), with the story as told by Walter Hartright:

It was the last day of July. The long hot summer was drawing to a close; and we, the weary pilgrims of the London pavement, were beginning to think of the cloud-shadows on the corn-fields, and the autumn breezes on the sea-shore.

For my own part, the fading summer left me out of health, out of spirits, and, if the truth must be told, out of money as well. During the past year I had not managed my professional resources as carefully as usual; and my extravagance now limited me to the prospect of spending the autumn economically between my mother's cottage at Hampstead and my own chambers in town.

The evening, I remember, was still and cloudy; the London air was at its heaviest; the distant hum of the street-traffic was at its faintest; the small pulse of the life within me, and the great heart of the city around me, seemed to be sinking in unison, languidly and more languidly, with the sinking sun. I roused myself from the book which I was dreaming over rather than reading, and left my chambers to meet the cool night air in the suburbs. It was one of the two evenings in every week which I was accustomed to spend with my mother and my sister. So I turned my steps northward in the direction of Hampstead.

Events which I have yet to relate make it necessary to mention in this place that my father had been dead some years at the period of which I am now writing; and that my sister Sarah and I were the sole survivors of a family of five children. My father was a drawing-master before me. His exertions had made him highly successful in his profession; and his affectionate anxiety to provide for the future of those who were dependent on his labours had impelled him, from the time of his marriage, to devote to the insuring of his life a much larger portion of his income than most men consider it necessary to set aside for that purpose. Thanks to his admirable prudence and self-denial my mother and sister were left, after his death, as independent of the world as they had been during his lifetime. I succeeded to his connection, and had every reason to feel grateful for the prospect that awaited me at my starting in life.

� Discussion

As a class Compare the opening scenes of the play, the TV adaptation and the novel.

- Why are the three versions so different?
- What information does the play audience need in the opening scene to understand what follows?
- What different ways are there of telling the audience what they need to know?
- Which version do you like best, and why? Could you improve it, and if so, how?

Writing

On your own Write your own opening scene for the play. Look for simple ways to capture the audience's attention. Remember that they do not need to know everything all at once. Where will you set the scene and how will it start? There are lots of possibilities, for example:

- the road to London, at night. Walter meets Anne Catherick.
- Walter's Mother's house. Pesca is waiting for Walter to come home to tell him the news about his appointment to Limmeridge.
- Blackwater Park. Fosco arrives, after being invited by Sir Percival.

The death of Sir Percival

Read the following extract from the novel, written from Walter Hartright's point of view.

I mounted the hill rapidly. The dark mass of the church-tower was the first object I discerned dimly against the night sky … The instant I turned the corner and came in view of the vestry, I saw the lantern-skylight on the roof brilliantly lit up from within. It shone out with dazzling brightness against the murky, starless sky.

I hurried through the churchyard to the door. As I got near there was a strange smell stealing out on the damp night air. I heard a snapping noise inside – I saw the light above grow brighter and brighter – a pane of the glass cracked – I ran to the door and put my hand on it. The vestry was on fire!

Before I could move, before I could draw my breath after that discovery, I was horror-struck by a heavy thump against the door from the inside. I heard the key worked violently in the lock – I heard a man's voice behind the door, raised to a dreadful shrillness, screaming for help.

The servant who had followed me staggered back shuddering, and dropped to his knees. "Oh, my God!" he said, "it's Sir Percival!"

As the words passed his lips the clerk joined us, and at the same moment there was another and a last grating turn of the key in the lock.

"The Lord have mercy on his soul!" said the old man. "He is doomed and dead. He has hampered the lock."

⟨⟨ ⟩⟩ Discussion

As a class Compare this account of the vestry fire with the version in the play (Act 3, Scene 6), noting the differences.

39

- Why do you think the story was changed in the play?
- Do you think the scene in the play is effective?
- Why?

✍ Writing

A. In groups Write your own stage version of the vestry fire scene, including whichever characters you think will help to make the scene dramatic. Think about how the scene might work on stage. (You might first want to read the chapter in the novel from which the extract is taken: 'The Third Epoch', Chapter 10).

B. On your own You are a newspaper reporter at the scene of the fire. Write a newspaper report for the front page of your newspaper, including the following:

(H)

- headline
- eyewitness accounts
- your own impressions
- why the fire started and who is to blame.

The life and times of Wilkie Collins

Wilkie Collins

Wilkie Collins was born in 1824, and brought up in London. He was the eldest child of the landscape artist, William Collins. Wilkie went to a local boarding school, Maida Hill Academy, which he hated. The school did not suit Wilkie's imaginative and intelligent nature. He had a strong will and was often punished for misbehaviour. He was bullied a great deal.

When he was thirteen the family moved to Italy. He rebelled against his father's conventional attitudes and strict religious beliefs, becoming a life-long radical and free-thinker. He was much closer to his mother, who sympathised with his creative ambitions.

Wilkie took a job in the office of a London tea-broker, while continuing to write by night. He was to receive endless rejections from publishers for full-length novels. Finally, his father allowed him to leave his employment and train to be a barrister.

In 1847 William Collins died. Wilkie Collins wrote a successful book about his painter father. Collins decided that he wanted to write more than anything else. In 1851 he met the novelist Charles Dickens, and the two men became great friends. They travelled together, encouraged each other with their writings and acted in plays together. *The Woman in White* was written in 1860 and was published in episodes in a magazine. It was an immediate popular success and was followed by *The Moonstone* in 1868. He was now rich and famous.

Wilkie Collins wrote over thirty novels, short stories and plays, but the quality of his writing gradually deteriorated. He suffered from gout from his early thirties, controlling the often intense pain with increasing amounts of opium. His addiction to the drug caused him to become obsessed with outlandish people and events, and his last books were full of gruesome characters.

Collins once said, "My life has been rather a strange one" – and it most certainly was! He lived with his mother until he was in his thirties and, although he never married, he had two mistresses and was the father of three children. His scandalous private life led to him being shut out from smart Victorian society. He suffered a heart-attack and died on 23 September 1889. He was sixty-five years old. He is now sometimes seen as the inventor of the detective novel.

✍ Writing

According to one of his friends, Wilkie Collins wrote *The Woman in White* after he saw "a young and very beautiful woman dressed in flowing white robes" run from the gates of a house in London. This was Caroline Graves, who would later become Collins's mistress. She had been kept prisoner in the house for several months by her violent husband.

On your own Write a short story of your own based around a strange encounter with a woman in white. The story begins:
"It was after midnight on a cold night. I shouldn't have been out walking that late, but the last bus had gone…"

H

The story of
The Woman In White

Walter Hartright, a young drawing master, has obtained a job at Limmeridge House, in Cumberland, to teach two young ladies. While walking home from Hampstead on his last evening in London, Walter meets a mysterious woman dressed in white. He helps her on her way but later learns she has escaped from an asylum.

The following day, he travels to Limmeridge House, where he meets Marian Halcombe and her half-sister Laura Fairlie. The owner of the house is their uncle Frederick Fairlie, a selfish hypochondriac (someone who keeps imagining they are ill), who shuts himself away from the world.

Walter is astonished to note Laura's resemblance to the woman in white, whose name Marian discovers is Anne Catherick. Anne was devoted to Laura's mother, who first dressed her in white.

Laura and Walter fall in love, but Laura has already promised her late father that she will marry a baronet, Sir Percival Glyde. Marian tells Walter to leave Limmeridge at once. Anne, meanwhile, sends a letter to Laura warning her against Sir Percival. She meets Walter and tells him Sir Percival was responsible for shutting her up in the asylum.

Laura and Sir Percival marry and journey to Italy, while Walter travels to South America, nursing a broken heart. Sir Percival and Laura, who is now Lady Glyde, return to Sir Percival's home, Blackwater Park in Hampshire, with Count Fosco. Marian Halcombe is invited to stay at Blackwater Park. She immediately distrusts the sinister Count Fosco. Sir Percival attempts to bully Laura into signing a document that would allow him to spend her marriage settlement of twenty thousand pounds.

Anne Catherick is seen in the grounds. She promises to reveal a secret to Laura that will ruin Sir Percival, but she is captured before she can do so. Marian overhears Sir Percival and Count Fosco talking, but she becomes ill with a fever before she can act on what she has heard.

Laura is tricked into travelling to London. Her identity is switched with Anne Catherick by Count Fosco. Anne dies of a heart attack and is buried in Cumberland. Laura is drugged and placed in an asylum under Anne's name. Sir Percival has stolen Laura's inheritance and, when Anne dies, Sir Percival takes Laura's money because people believe it is Laura who is dead. When Marian recovers from her illness, she tracks Laura down and rescues her from the asylum, but both women are now poor.

Walter Hartright returns from America and is told of what has happened. Walter sets out to discover Sir Percival's secret, concealed by a forged entry in the marriage register in Blackwater Church. As Walter closes in on the truth – that Sir Percival is illegitimate and not the baronet he claims to be – Sir Percival tries to have Walter followed. He burns the register, but the church vestry, packed with dry material, catches fire and Sir Percival burns to death. Before he dies, he reveals that Anne was the illegitimate child of Laura's father, Mr Fairlie, which is why the two women looked alike.

Walter Hartright discovers that Count Fosco is a member of a secret Italian society, the Brotherhood, which he has betrayed, and to which Professor Pesca also belongs. Hartright forces Count Fosco to write a confession and Laura's identity is restored. Walter Hartright and Laura marry. Laura's uncle, Frederick Fairlie, dies soon after and leaves Laura and Walter the Limmeridge estate.

🎭 Story-telling

In groups Divide the story into episodes, and give each episode a title (for example: 'Walter Meets the Woman in White'; 'Laura at Blackwater Park'; 'Walter's Return'). Write the titles on separate slips of paper and share these out among the group. Tell the story to the class, in your own words, with each person telling the parts of the story that are on their slips.

Themes within and around the play

MARRIAGE AND THE LAW

Married Women's Rights

One of the reasons why Wilkie Collins wrote *The Woman in White* was his belief that married women were treated unjustly under English law. Wives had almost no rights, no possessions, and no protection against cruel treatment by their husbands. In 1860:

● *A married woman owned no property*
Anything the woman had owned before she married (such as money, jewellery, clothes, furniture) now belonged to her husband, and was his to do with as he pleased.

● *A married woman had no legal existence*
A man and wife were treated as the same person under the law. She had no independent rights, she could not defend her own interests in court, and was not held responsible for her own actions.

● *A married woman could not keep her own earnings*
Any money earned by a married woman belonged entirely to her husband.

● *A mother had no rights over her children*
The father had legal custody over her children, and could take them from her if he chose. If the parents were legally separated, the father had right of custody.

● *A wife could not divorce her husband for adultery*
A man had only to prove that his wife had been unfaithful. A woman had to prove adultery, plus "aggravating offences". In practice, it was almost impossible for a woman to divorce her husband.

The Married Women's Property Acts

By the 1860s, the movement to gain legal rights for women, and to allow them access to education and the professions, was beginning to gain ground. A women's petition to parliament stated:

"… it is time that … in entering the state of marriage, [women] no longer pass from freedom into the condition of a slave, all of whose earnings belong to his master and not to himself."

In 1870, the first Married Women's Property Act allowed wives to keep their own earnings. It was a first, small step towards full equality. In 1882, a second act gave women the right to keep all their own property.

Marriage today

Married couples are now treated as equals under the law. In divorce cases, custody of children usually goes to the mother. Each partner has a right to a share in the property they buy together, and most couples share their earnings.

Around one in three marriages in England and Wales now end in divorce. Some couples have taken to drawing up 'pre-nuptial agreements', in which the man and woman agree before they marry how their property will be divided up, in the event that the marriage breaks down.

☾☽ Discussion

As a class

- What do you think of pre-nuptial agreements?
- Is it just common sense for couples to plan for the possibility of divorce, or does making a plan make divorce more likely?
- Why do people choose to get married if so many marriages break down?

☻☻ Role Play

Organisation Work in pairs, taking opposite views from your partner – the views you take don't have to be your own views.

Situation A young couple are talking about buying a house together. She has a job and he doesn't. The man says they should get married first.

Opening line WOMAN: "But that's so old-fashioned."

✍ Writing

Read the information on page 62. Imagine that Laura has asked the family lawyer, Mr Gilmore, for advice on her rights, after Sir Percival tried to get her to sign the documents. Use the information to write a letter from Mr Gilmore to Laura, advising her of her rights as a married woman.

THE TREATMENT OF MENTAL ILLNESS

When Walter Hartright meets Anne Catherick for the first time, at the beginning of *The Woman in White*, she has escaped from a private asylum near London. She is terrified that she will be recaptured and forced to return. The novel is set around 1850. What would the institution she escaped from have been like?

Victorian asylums

The Victorian age saw a revolution in the treatment of the mentally ill. John Connolly, head of Hanwell Asylum, remembered:

> …gloomy mansions in which hands and feet were daily bound with straps or chains… The patients were a defenceless flock, at the mercy of men and women who were habitually severe, often cruel, and sometimes brutal… Cold apartments, beds of straw, meagre diet, scanty clothing, scanty bedding, darkness, pestilent air, sickness and suffering, and medical neglect – all these were common… No mercy, no pity, no decent regard for affliction, for age, or for sex, existed. Old and young, men and women, the frantic and the melancholy, were treated worse, and more neglected, than the beasts of the field.

Connolly and other reformers persuaded parliament to build large new public asylums in which physical restraint and cruelty would no longer be practised. The new asylums were planned as complete, self-contained communities in which the inmates would recover their senses through 'moral management', which meant useful work, religion and clean living. A doctor described an ideal asylum like this:

You meet the gardener, the common agriculturist, the mower, the weeder, all intent on their several occupations, and loud in their merriment. The flowers are tended, and trained, and watered by one, the humbler task of preparing the vegetables for the table is committed to another... [there are] companies of straw-plaiters, basket-makers, knitters, spinners, among the women ... weavers, tailors, saddlers and shoemakers among the men... They literally work to please themselves, and having once experienced the possibility of doing this, a difficulty is found in restraining their eagerness, and moderating their exertions.

The proof of this happiness and harmony was shown to the public in the 'lunatics' ball', a regular event at many public asylums, in which the inmates could be watched dancing cheerfully together.

Katherine Drake, "Lunatics' Ball, Somerset," *1848*

In reality, however, life in the asylums was far from ideal. Every aspect of the patients' lives was strictly controlled, with misbehaviour often punished with long periods of solitary confinement. As the numbers in the asylums grew, they became less like communities and more like prisons, with confinement and monotonous routine taking the place of care and treatment.

On your own Using the above extract, write an imaginary account of a day in Anne Catherick's life in the asylum. This would have been a much smaller institution than the one described, with inmates from better-off families, but it might have been run along similar lines. The novel describes the grounds of the asylum as: "prettily laid out … a turf walk, shaded by a shrubbery on either side". But we know it was not easy for Anne or Laura to escape.

The inmates of the public asylums were mostly poor. Better-off families would go to great lengths to conceal mental illness and avoid having relatives committed to the public asylums. The mentally ill were sent to smaller, private asylums – like the one where Anne Catherick and Laura are sent – or kept at home. In *Jane Eyre*, by Charlotte Brontë, the wife of Jane's employer, Rochester, is kept locked up in secret in an attic:

In a room without a window, there burnt a fire, guarded by a high and strong fender, and a lamp suspended from the ceiling by a chain. Grace Poole bent over the fire, apparently cooking something in a saucepan. In the deep shade, at the farther end of the room, a figure ran backwards and forewards. What it was, whether beast or human being, one could not, at first sight tell: it grovelled, seemingly, on all fours; it snatched and growled like some strange animal: but it was covered with clothing, and a quantity of dark, grizzled hair, wild as a mane, hid its head and face.

☺☺ Discussion

In groups
- What does the extract aboove tell us about how Mrs Rochester has been cared for?
- What does it suggest about the author's attitude to mental illness?

The private asylum in which Anne and Laura were kept might have looked like the women's gallery at Bethlehem Hospital, known as 'Bedlam' (top; 1890). The garden of the hospital of Sainte Anne, Paris (below; 1871) gives an idea of the one in which Marian found Laura in the identity of Anne in the novel.

Wrongful confinement

As more asylums were built in Britain, the fear that sane people could be wrongly confined by their relatives took hold of people's imaginations. In *Hard Cash* by Charles Reade, written three years after *The Woman in White*, the hero is tricked with a forged letter into entering a private lunatic asylum. He finds himself in

---

a very long room... the unpapered walls were a cold drab, and wanted washing... The servant retired into the drawing room, closing the door softly after him: once closed it became invisible; it fitted like wax, and left nothing to be seen but books; not even a knob... he went to take a book from the shelves.

He found it was a piece of iron, admirably painted... he went to a door... but it was blocked up... Alfred was a prisoner.

✐ Writing

On your own Continue the story to the point where Alfred attempts to escape, bringing in lots of further details about the room. There is a means of escape from the room, but it will not be easy for Alfred to find.

The case of Louisa Lowe

Louisa Lowe was a middle-aged woman trapped in a loveless marriage to George Lowe, a Devonshire vicar. Isolated, lonely and suspicious of her husband, who she thought was unfaithful to her, she became a convinced spiritualist, able, she thought, to communicate with the spirits of the dead.

Finally, her spirits gave her the courage to leave her husband. She moved into lodgings in Exeter, where two medical men, friends of her husband, found her and had her committed to a private lunatic asylum. She was to remain in the asylum for the next year and a half, and was only released because her husband's impatience to get possession of her money brought the case into public view. She had written hundreds of letters to try and gain her release, like this one to the Lunacy Commissioners:

I am indefinitely re-consigned to this hideous doom – this lingering death in life, this moral torture of incarceration among maniacs… Do you, of your own knowledge and from personal observation, certify me, at the present time, legally and technically a lunatic? If not, when was I last one? In what day or in what month did I commit my last insane act?… I DENY that I am mad.

As we saw, in the section on law and marriage, wives were at this time still very vulnerable at the hands of unscrupulous husbands.

An inmate of a lunatic asylum and a nurse (1885)

Louisa Lowe became a committed campaigner for the reform of the lunacy laws. In her book, *The Bastilles of England,* she estimated that there were

…more than 20,000 persons in England and Wales not only deprived, without cause, of all civil rights; but subjected to… slavery on false allegations of lunacy; in fact, condemned, and perhaps for life, to a doom worse than a felon's without trial, or even knowing [why] they are accused.

Research and Presentation

On your own There were many women and men in the Victorian age who became famous as pioneers and reformers (for example: Florence Nightingale, who worked to reform hospital care; Elizabeth Garrett Anderson, the first woman doctor in England; Lord Shaftesbury, who fought to abolish child labour in the coal-mines). Prepare and give a short presentation to the class on the life and work of one of these people. Use an encyclopedia at your local library to get you started.

Care in the community

In the 1980s, parliament decided to close down the remaining Victorian asylums and help the patients to return to a more normal life in the world outside. The policy became known as 'care in the community'. In 1998, after a series of tragic events, the policy was abandoned. Read the extract below, taken from an article in *The Independent.*

THE GOVERNMENT "drew a line" under care in the community yesterday, saying it had let down both patients and public and must be replaced with a "tough and effective" regime.

Patients will in future be forced to comply with treatment and the focus will be on 24-hour care, with more specialist secure units and new outreach teams who will keep track of psychiatric patients.

Yesterday's announcement signals the end of the policy of care in the community, although the Government promised there would be no return to "locking up patients ... in long-stay institutions".

It comes after a succession of inquiries into killings by psychiatric patients, such as that of Jonathon Zito, who was stabbed by Christopher Clunis, a paranoid schizophrenic, at a London Underground station in 1992. One survey estimated such killings happened once every two weeks. This is dwarfed by the harm that patients do to themselves, with 1,000 suicides a year.

"Discharging people from institutions has brought benefits to some," the Secretary of State for Health, Frank Dobson, said. "Others have been left to become a danger to themselves and a nuisance to others. Too many confused and sick people have been left wandering the streets... A small but significant minority have become a danger to the public as well as themselves."

The director of the Mental Health Foundation, June McKerrow, said: "This is a real chance to wipe the slate clean and rectify so many problems which have prevented community care from succeeding in the first place."

☺✍ **Presentation**

In groups Present a short summary, in your own words, of:

- what the article is about
- the most important facts in the article
- the views of the people quoted.

Mental illness

Around one in seven adults are hit by some form of mental illness during their lifetime, often due to stress, or because of bad experiences. Most illnesses are short-lived, but they can be frightening, both to the sufferer and to their families. There are two broad categories of mental illness:

- **Neurosis**, which is when a person's normal emotions and reactions become exaggerated. It is much more common than psychosis, and is often minor. Neurotic illnesses include anxiety and depression.

- **Psychosis**, which is more serious, usually requiring medical treatment. In psychosis, some aspect of reality is distorted, with the sufferer experiencing delusions or hallucinations. Schizophrenia is a psychotic illness.

Neurotic illnesses can give rise to phobias, obsessions and compulsions, and eating disorders. Here are some people's stories.

Shaheena (aged 30) "I became depressed after my first baby. I kept thinking little Asha would die. I broke down in tears and saw the doctor. It took me quite a while to recover, but I am well again now."

Kevin (aged 16) "I developed a compulsion during my GCSE year. I had to tidy my bedroom all the time, I just could not sleep unless everything was in place. Sometimes, I would wake up at two in the morning and start to tidy up. My mum understood because she'd had a compulsion once, she just had to wash her hands all the time. All I needed was rest!"

Jason (aged 19) "I used to think I was dying of cancer because my throat was tight and I felt I could not swallow. I thought the doctors were not telling me the truth when they gave me tests and said I was fine. I'm well again now, and at university, but it was hard to go through my obsession at the time."

Saleema (aged 16) "I used to think I was fat. I started slimming and went too far. If my parents forced me to eat, I made myself sick. I still worry about my weight, but I do eat regularly and I am well again."

🎭 **Role Play**

Organisation Work in pairs.

Situation A counsellor is in a counselling session with a young person, who is worried about one of the problems described above. It is their first visit.

Opening line COUNSELLOR: "Do you want to tell me about it?"

Extension Share your scene with the rest of the class, and ask for their comments and suggestions.

SYMBOLISM

Symbols are visual images which represent abstract ideas, for example: scales represent justice; a lion represents strength and courage; a dove represents peace. Actions and gestures can also be symbolic, for example: a clenched fist can symbolise rebellion.

In literature, writers use symbolism to show the deeper meaning of events. In *Macbeth*, for example, Shakespeare uses repeated images of blood to represent guilt and remorse. Lady Macbeth, tortured by her secret guilt at the murder of the king, Duncan, tries endlessly to wash the blood off her hands as she sleepwalks.

DOCTOR What is it she does now? Look, how she rubs her hands.

GENTLEWOMAN It is an accustomed action with her, to seem thus washing her hands. I have known her to continue in this a quarter of an hour.

LADY MACBETH Yet here's a spot.

DOCTOR Hark! She speaks. I will set down what comes from her, to satisfy my remembrance the more strongly.

LADY MACBETH Out damned spot! out, I say! One; two: why then, 'tis time to do't. Hell is murky! Fie, my lord, fie! a soldier, and afeard? What need we fear who knows it, when none can

72

call our power to account? Yet who would have thought the old man to have had so much blood in him?

Doctor Do you mark that?

Lady Macbeth The Thane of Fife had a wife: where is she now? What! Will these hands ne'er be clean? ...

✐ Writing

Write a short story in which a character sleepwalks and another character watchers him/her. The sleepwalker might reveal something he/she has kept secret, like Lady Macbeth does.

The Woman in White, with its saintly heroes and wicked villains, uses symbolism to heighten the contrast between right and wrong, virtue and wickedness.

☺ ☺ Discussion

- What do you think might be the symbolic meaning of Fosco's canaries?
- Why does the author choose to kill off Sir Percival in a church?
- Look for other possible symbols in the play.

In the following extract from *The Woman in Black* by Susan Hill, the narrator is attending a funeral, when he sees a stranger come into the church.

It was indeed a melancholy little service, with so few of us in the cold church... However, towards the end of it, and on hearing some slight rustle behind me, I half-turned, discreetly, and caught a glimpse of another mourner, a woman, who must have slipped into the church... and who stood several rows behind and quite alone, very erect and still, and not holding a prayer book. She was dressed in deepest black, in the style of full mourning... A bonnet-type hat covered her head and shaded her face, but, although I did not stare, even the swift glance I took of the woman showed me enough to recognise that she was suffering from some

terrible wasting disease, for not only was she extremely pale...
but the skin and, it seemed, only the thinnest layer of flesh was
tautly stretched and strained across her bones, so that it gleamed
with a curious, blue-white sheen, and her eyes seemed sunken
back into her head.

And then I looked up away from the woman and back, to where
the coffin was being lowered into the ground... When I looked
up again, I saw a blackbird on the hollybush a few feet away and
heard him open his mouth to pour out a sparkling fountain of song
in the November sunlight, and then it was all over, we were
moving away from the graveside... I intended to wait for the
sick-looking woman and offer my arm to escort her. But she was
nowhere to be seen.

☺☺ Discussion

A. In groups Read the extract above.

- Is there a symbolic reason why the woman is dressed in black,
  beyond the fact that she is attending a funeral?
- What might the blackbird and the sunlight represent?

B. Why does Wilkie Collins call his novel *The Woman in White*?

- Is there a symbolic meaning in that choice of colour?
- Make a list of as many symbolic uses of the colour white as you
  can think of.

☺☺ Discussion

In pairs Read the poem below.

- What symbols are used and what do they represent?
- What is the poem telling us about love?

'Waly, Waly' (traditional)

The water is wide, I cannot cross,
And neither have I wings to fly.
Bring me a boat that will carry two,
And we shall row, my love and I.

cont...

O down in the meadow the other day,
When gathering flowers bright and gay,
When gathering flowers red and blue,
I little thought what love could do.

I put my hand into a bush,
Thinking the fairest flower to find.
I pricked my finger to the bone
And left the fairest flower behind.

I leaned my back against an oak,
Thinking it was a trusty tree;
But first it bent and then it broke,
And so did my false love to me.

There is a ship that sails the sea,
She's loaded deep as deep can be,
But not so deep as the love I'm in;
I know not if I sink or swim.

O love is handsome and love is fine;
And love's a jewel while it is new;
But when it is old it's growing cold,
And fades away like morning dew.

✍ Writing

Write your own poem or story making use of symbols. Try to think up
new symbols, rather than using familiar ones.

H

Research resources

The Secret Life of Wilkie Collins by William M. Clarke (Allison & Busby)
The Moonstone by Wilkie Collins (Penguin)
The Woman in Black by Susan Hill (Longman)

Victorian Asylums
The Female Malady by Elaine Showalter (Virago)

Louisa Lowe
The Darkened Room by Alex Owen (Virago)